The Great Sand Hills
A Prairie Oasis

The Great Sand Hills
A Prairie Oasis

Text by Rebecca L. Grambo   Photographs by Branimir Gjetvaj

Nature Saskatchewan
206 - 1860 Lorne St.
Regina, Saskatchewan S4P 2L7

Published by Nature Saskatchewan, Special Publication No. 26

Grambo, Rebecca L. (1963 -   )

The Great Sand Hills: A Prairie Oasis

Includes bibliographical references and index

ISBN: 0-921104-22-7

1. Great Sand Hills (Sask.)—History. 2. Natural history—Saskatchewan—
Great Sand Hills. 3. Prairie ecology—Saskatchewan—Great Sand Hills.
4. Endangered ecosystems—Saskatchewan—Great Sand Hills. I. Gjetvaj,
Branimir, (1960-   ) II. Nature Saskatchewan III. Title. IV. Series: Special publication
(Nature Saskatchewan) ; 26.

FC3545.G72G73 2007   971.24'3   C2007-900738-4

Cover and interior design by The Noblet Group, Regina, Saskatchewan

Printed and bound in Canada at Friesens Corporation, Altona, Manitoba

All photographs in the book, except those credited within the book to other photographers, are by Branimir
Gjetvaj

The satellite photograph which appears on page 8 is used courtesy of TerraServer®.com

The map of the Great Sand Hills which appears on page 8 is used with the permission of the Department of
Saskatchewan Environment

The archival photograph on page 29 is used with the permission of the Saskatchewan Archives

Photographs by Glen and Rebecca Grambo appear on pages 64, 66, 67, 69, 114, and 116

The image of the Ord's Kangaroo Rat on page 70 is by David Gummer and is used courtesy of the Royal
Alberta Museum in Edmonton

Nature Saskatchewan gratefully acknowledges the support for the production of this book as provided by the
Saskatchewan Heritage Foundation and The Cultural Industries Development Fund (Department of Culture,
Youth & Recreation) which is administered by the Saskatchewan Publishers Group. Nature Saskatchewan
also acknowledges the support from Saskatchewan Lotteries.

To order directly from the publisher, please add $5.50 (shipping and handling in Canada) to the price of the
first copy and $2.00 to each additional copy up to a maximum of $16. Send cheque or money order to:

Nature Saskatchewan
206 -1860 Lorne St.
Regina, SK S4P SL7

For more information about Nature Saskatchewan and its publications go to: www.naturesask.ca

TABLE OF CONTENTS

ACKNOWLEDGMENTS

Without exception, the people I called, visited, and emailed while working on this book lived up to the generous reputation of prairie folk. I stopped people in cafes, on the streets, in grocery stores, and at the Great Sandhills Museum & Interpretive Centre in Sceptre to ask them about the Great Sand Hills. The subject may have been contentious but my reception was always warm. My thanks to all of you for your patience and your coffee. Several people provided exceptional assistance. Randy Lawrence offered invaluable documents and encouragement. Eleanor Bowie shared both her hospitality and her opinions with wonderful openness. Lawrence Townley-Smith took time to answer a ton of questions, including many completely unrelated to this project but important to an author off on a tangent. Edwin Small Legs shared his feelings about the Great Sand Hills and why they are important to the Blackfoot people. David Gummer contributed fascinating information about kangaroo rats. Kevin Fitzsimonds, Kerry Wrishko, John Wagner, David Gauthier, Joe Schmutz, Ken Dahl, Karyn Scalise, Brian Mathieson, Andrea Kotylak, and Dean Smith filled in data gaps and supplied reference information. My devoted corps of proofreaders—Marlene Kozak, Cory Cox, Glen Grambo—did their best to squelch the printing gremlins. Any errors in the text, factual or typographical, can be dropped squarely in my lap. Besides contributing his photographic skills, my husband, Glen, took over the household duties, and brought me a new keyboard when I sneezed and spilled cold medicine into mine. I also can't say a big enough "thank you" to the hard-working people at Nature Saskatchewan, for taking this book on trust and a handshake. Thanks to the team at The Noblet Design Group for doing excellent work despite a tight schedule. And, finally, to Branimir—thanks for not taking "I'm too busy" for an answer, for introducing me to the Sand Hills, and for being incredibly good about not pestering me while I was struggling with the manuscript. This book exists because you made it happen.

— Rebecca L. Grambo

Our gratitude goes to Ian and Eleanor Bowie, Neil and Denise Block, and Robin Wiggins for allowing access to their land so we could photograph the most spectacular landscapes in the Great Sand Hills. When the nights turned too cold to sleep "in the bush," the Bowie and Block families provided shelter and many warm cups of coffee that kept me on life support. Their hospitality and friendship was invaluable for completion of this project. Jason Gizen skillfully piloted his small plane allowing me to take aerial photographs of the open sand dunes. Many thanks to Jason for his patience with my numerous requests to change direction, and for leaving the plane windows open to allow for that perfect shot. Stewart Bosch facilitated cattle round-up photography in Heck Co-op pasture. Glen and Rebecca Grambo contributed several superb wildlife images, and David Gummer provided images of the Ord's Kangaroo Rat. The map of the Great Sand Hills is courtesy of Saskatchewan Environment. Arlene and Robin Karpan gave me a head start in understanding intricate details of book publishing, while Anna Leighton shared her expertise in plant identification. I am also grateful to the many people who showed interest in this project and provided encouragement along the way.

— Branimir Gjetvaj

INTRODUCTION

The prairies are and always have been my home, the place in which I feel most comfortable. You can see things here. Land and sky are open to your questioning senses. Spring arrives with the first meadowlark's song and fall is signaled by the sounds of migrating geese and sandhill cranes. The weather sets the tempo and tone of life.

I took my "inner prairie" with me when my life carried me to new places and jobs: graduating as a Geological Engineer in the Black Hills of South Dakota; sweating as a roustabout in the West Texas oilfields; crunching numbers as a geophysicist in Houston, Texas; tracking contaminant plumes in the groundwater in Silicon Valley. When I moved to Saskatoon in 1986 to study hydrogeology in glacial aquifers at the University of Saskatchewan, I was very happy to be back "home." I had no idea that these varied experiences would later prove invaluable for learning and writing about Saskatchewan's Great Sand Hills.

When I began my research on the area, I was aware of its present natural riches but not of its history, which became more intriguing with each new bit of information I learned. The Great Sand Hills seemed to sit in an eye of the post-contact cultural and ecological hurricane, definitely touched by the sweeping changes around them but not nearly as much as the surrounding lands. This phenomenon helps to explain why they remain so ecologically and archaeologically rich today. For that reason—and just because the facts are so interesting in themselves—I felt it important to share what I learned. The first portion of this book, therefore, travels from the birth of the Great Sand Hills to the present.

Of course, attempting to describe the comings and goings in a place for 15,000 years or so creates some unique problems. Different sources disagree on dates, sometimes by a year, sometimes by five thousand years. I have chosen what I felt were the most reliable and sensible figures. Names of people and places change, groups come together and split, often many times. For simplicity's sake and to make it easier for those checking references, I have used the names of various First Nations as they are given in historical sources rather than the current names. Those referred to as the Blackfoot people are actually three distinct nations that share a language, a land base, and a history: the Kainai (Blood), the Northern and Southern Piikani (Piegan) and the Siksika (Black-sole or Blackfoot). The Southern Piikani, also known as the Amsskaapipikani, live in the United States and are commonly called the Blackfeet Tribe of Montana. The Sioux people of Chief Sitting Bull are now known as the Hunkpapa Lakota. Simply because of space and time restrictions, I have had to focus on those most strongly associated with the Great Sand Hills rather than trying to catalog all who had contact with them.

Because they could not be farmed successfully, the Great Sand Hills escaped much of the intensive alteration that affected the arable land surrounding them during the last hundred years. They remained relatively untouched, used mainly for grazing by ranchers driven by economics to be good stewards. The middle

4

section of this volume gives you a look at the land, plants, animals, and people that co-exist in the Great Sand Hills today.

In the 1960s, the TransCanada pipeline cut through the hills, leaving a scar behind despite strong efforts to restore the land to its original condition. Then, in the late 1970s, natural gas exploration and development began in the area. A spurt of seismic work and well drilling followed in the 1980s, each project inflicting its own disruption and damage. Every new access road provided another opportunity for hunters and tourists to reach back country areas. When a photograph of the Great Sand Hills appeared on the cover of phone books across the province, interest in the area rose sharply but so did the vehicle traffic. The conflict over what was happening escalated and spread beyond the local population. The crux of the debate was this: development of this resource could put money for badly needed services and infrastructure into government coffers, but the extremely fragile Sand Hills landscape and its unique ecosystem could be damaged irreparably.

Several planning committees, land use strategies, and moratoria later, the basic conflict remains the same and it has grown rather than gone away. As I write these words, work is progressing on the Great Sand Hills Regional Environmental Study (GSHRES). Slated to be completed in 2007, the GSHRES has been gathering data about the social, environmental, and economic factors associated with the Great Sand Hills. From that information, the scientists will generate risk assessments for various human activities in the area. Using the risk factors they calculate, they will play through several scenarios for the future of the Great Sand Hills, using different combinations of development and ecological preservation strategies. Finally, the GSHRES Scientific Advisory Committee will make recommendations about the best options for preserving the ecological integrity of the Great Sand Hills. The final portion of this book discusses some of the main challenges and possibilities that the Committee, the Government of Saskatchewan, and all other interested parties must consider.

The Great Sand Hills Regional Environmental Study is a very good thing despite its limitations (e.g. no mammal or reptile surveys). Intelligent decisions about the future of the Great Sand Hills can only be made using the best and most complete information possible. But statistics and facts can be cold things, unable to convey unquantifiable but valuable qualities, just as the accurately measured open space on the Saskatchewan map labeled "Great Sand Hills" gives no true idea of the living land it represents. This book is an attempt to put flesh on the bones, to give readers a sample of the uncountable riches that the Great Sand Hills embrace: their place in First Nations spiritual beliefs and in the stories of the homesteaders, their abundant and varied plant and animal life, their presence as a living part of the ranching economy and daily life. As you read, consider all that the Great Sand Hills have been, are . . . and may yet be.

the Past

When Ice Ruled the Prairies

It seems strange to find sand dunes in southwestern Saskatchewan. After all, we're not exactly occupying beach-front property. The Great Sand Hills, along with the other approximately 120 sand dune complexes found on the Canadian prairies and those prairies themselves, are a left-behind landscape—the legacy of ice.

Beginning about 1.8 million years ago—at the start of what are commonly called the Ice Ages—a series of ice sheets came and went across North America and Europe, growing or contracting as the climate varied. When more precipitation fell at the head of the glaciers than melted at the advancing toes, the ice sheets expanded. If there was more ice melting than what was being added, the ice sheets grew smaller. Holding an ice cube in your hand, it is hard to imagine how ice could have much effect on the landscape. But during the Wisconsin glaciation, which happened from about 70,000 to 17,000 years ago, the ice sheets were 3 to 4 kilometers thick and took up enough water to lower world sea level by about 120 meters. Parts of northern North America and Europe are *still* rising slowly as they recover from the weight of that ice.

At least four major glaciation episodes—of which the Wisconsin was the last—sent ice sheets plowing across Saskatchewan. Since each new advance of the ice scoured away and buried evidence of previous glaciations, the landscape we see is mainly a creation of the Wisconsin glaciers—much of it in the form of a dying bequest. As the ice relentlessly ground and gouged its way over the land, it ripped up soil and rocks, pushing some out of the way and carrying others along beneath it, on top of it, or within it. Everything from fine powdery silt to rocks the size of houses rode along with the ice, some of the material travelling great distances. Today, boulders broken from the bones of the Canadian Shield hunker incongruously in prairie pastures, abandoned by retreating ice.

6

A lichen-covered glacial erratic rests among prairie grasses.

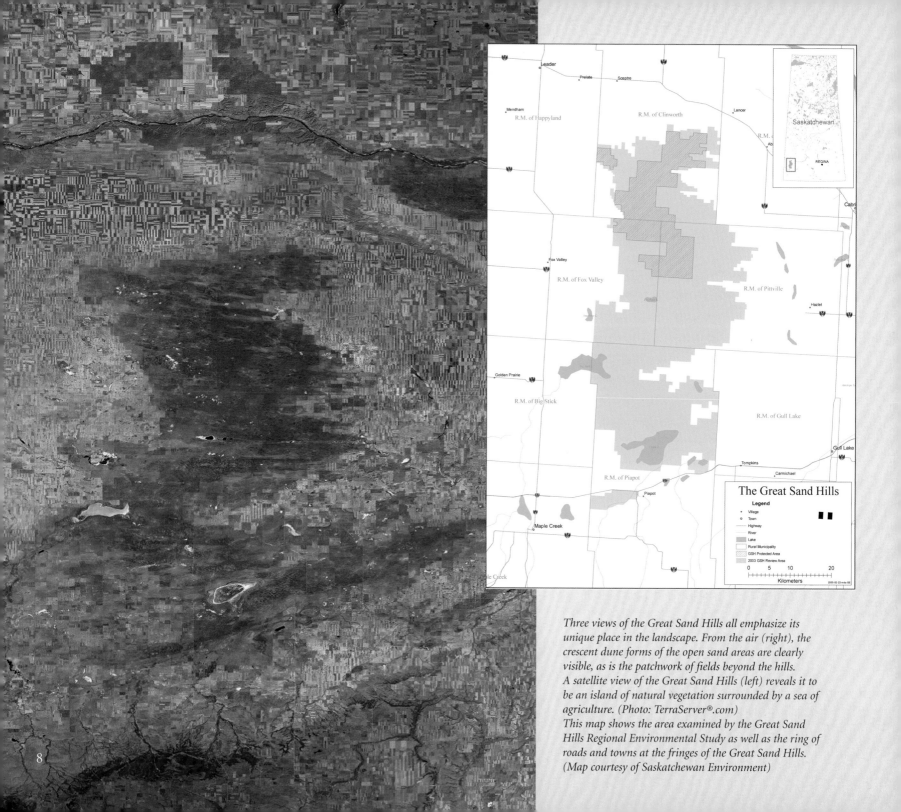

The Great Sand Hills

Legend

+ Village
○ Town
— Highway
River
Lake
Rural Municipality
GSH Protected Area
2003 GSH Review Area

0   5   10   20
Kilometers

R.M. of Happyland
R.M. of Clinworth
R.M. of Fox Valley
R.M. of Pittville
R.M. of Big Stick
R.M. of Gull Lake
R.M. of Piapot

Leader
Prelate
Sceptre
Mendham
Lancer
Fox Valley
Hazlet
Golden Prairie
Gull Lake
Tompkins
Carmichael
Maple Creek
Piapot

Saskatchewan
REGINA

Three views of the Great Sand Hills all emphasize its unique place in the landscape. From the air (right), the crescent dune forms of the open sand areas are clearly visible, as is the patchwork of fields beyond the hills.
A satellite view of the Great Sand Hills (left) reveals it to be an island of natural vegetation surrounded by a sea of agriculture. (Photo: TerraServer®.com)
This map shows the area examined by the Great Sand Hills Regional Environmental Study as well as the ring of roads and towns at the fringes of the Great Sand Hills. (Map courtesy of Saskatchewan Environment)

The gradual withdrawal of the ice began about 17,000 years ago when the climactic pendulum swung again. The great ice sheets began shrinking, leaving an altered landscape behind them. But it wasn't a smooth, continuous process. Along the ice front, the ice made numerous minor advances and retreats like an aging celebrity making just one more final appearance.

During the glacial retreat, the ice front was definitely where the action was. Glaciers function like conveyor belts, with ice constantly moving out from the head towards the front. Even while the boundary of the ice sheets retreated, the ice itself was still moving forward toward the front, carrying its rocky load of sediment and bulldozing stony debris ahead of it as well. Sometimes chunks of rotting ice broke off and melted, each leaving behind a pile of sand and gravel. At the front, melting ice dumped its burden, leaving behind vast deposits of mixed silt, sand, gravel and rock. Variations in the amount of time the ice front stayed in one place and in the sediment the melting ice dropped created uneven deposits, forming the rolling hills that make up part of today's prairie landscape.

Vast quantities of water poured out from the melting glaciers. Just like rushing streams and rivers today, the melt waters carried clay, silt, sand and gravel. As the streams moved away from their source, they lost energy and began to drop their sediment load. The coarser, heavier particles fell out first forming fan-shaped outwash plains of sand and gravel near to the ice front. Clay and silts were carried farther downstream.

At that time, the natural drainage of the land lay to the north and east, and the glacial waters tried to follow that pattern. The Wisconsin glaciers were withdrawing in that direction, however, and the ice formed a barrier. With nowhere to go, the rivers of meltwater backed up, creating then feeding huge lakes. The waters slowed when they reached the lakes, dropping the fine sediment they were carrying. When the glacial lakes eventually dried up, they left behind flat silt and clay deposits that became Canada's prime wheat growing areas. Saskatchewan's famous gumbo soil is lake-bottom mud.

There are other reminders of those vast lakes around as well. If you've ever thought the Qu'Appelle River seems pretty puny for the valley it occupies—you're right. The valley is a glacial spillway cut by the torrential runoff from glacial Lake Regina around 14,000 years ago and the present-day river a mere suggestion of its mighty predecessor.

As the ice continued to retreat, the land left behind was at the mercy of the climate. The wind scoured the bare plains of silt and sand, sweeping a storm of sediment across the landscape. In some scattered areas, when the wind released its hold, it left behind vast dune fields. The wind created the Great Sand Hills and they still respond to its touch.

The Great Herds and Their Hunters

The warming climate that forced the retreat of the glaciers brought about other changes as well. By about 12,000 years ago, the area that would become mixed-grass prairie in Saskatchewan was ice-free. Spruce forests that had grown along the ice front withdrew northward in the wake of the glaciers, yielding to grasses and parklands. Camels, horses and mammoths adapted for an Ice Age life slowly disappeared, vanishing completely by about 11,500 years ago. The people of the Clovis culture, mammoth and mastodon hunters who lived roughly 11,500 to 10,500 years ago, left behind large spearpoints as evidence of their passing through Saskatchewan but as their prey disappeared, so did their culture.

By about 9,500 years ago, the Saskatchewan climate was becoming similar to that of today. A new group of grazers, dominated by bison (commonly known as buffalo), had evolved to take advantage of the rapidly expanding grasslands. And a new type of culture, one based on hunting bison, emerged. It would grow and flourish until its prey base, too, disappeared.

The first buffalo hunts probably consisted of a group of hunters with spears confronting a lone animal. Because of the never-ending arms race between predator and prey, this early bison hunting scenario would undergo several transformations as time progressed, thanks to changes in human hunting technology and in the bison itself.

The huge, long-horned, Ice Age bison could stand and face the lone ambush predators it encountered, including saber-toothed cats and short-faced bears. A surprising turn of speed allowed it to escape from chasing hunters such as gray and dire wolves. After the dire wolves became extinct, packs of gray wolves were the main threat to bison. Gray wolves aren't particularly fast but they can keep running for quite a while and are tenacious in pursuit of a meal. For the bison, speed became less important than endurance. They became smaller and evolved powerful legs capable of propelling them over uneven ground until any pursuers tired and quit. Another strong pressure was also selecting for smaller, shyer bison. The big, fat, bold, healthy, bull bison were the ones most likely to stand and face a threat, which made them the easiest for human hunters to spear and kill. Long horns for close-in fighting were no longer an advantage either so they grew smaller, too. By about 5,000 years ago, bison were only about two-thirds the size of their Ice Age predecessors.

The open grasslands that appeared after the retreat of the ice sheets furnished food for many grazers. Human hunters following the herds gradually developed a culture centered around the dominant species— bison—which provided them with food, clothing, and shelter.

13

"We all see that the day is coming when the buffalo will all be killed, and we shall have nothing more to live on…then you will come into our camp and see the poor Blackfoot starving." —Crowfoot 1876

The human hunters' response to these changes in their prey are reflected in a rich variety of archaeological finds in the Great Sand Hills. Because of their unique mix of habitats and therefore, resources, the Great Sand Hills have always attracted people. Sites there tell stories of periodic occupation dating as far back as 11,000 years ago to as recently as the 1800s. Along with artifacts and information from other sites in southern Saskatchewan, these discoveries provide snapshots of the buffalo culture from birth to death.

At the Heron Eden site near Prelate, archaeologists uncovered a nearly 9,000-year-old bison kill site: evidence of hunters using heavy stone-tipped spears to kill large bison. The size of the bison bones suggests they may have been a now-extinct, extra-large species. Although scientists are just beginning to learn about the details of the site, it appears that the hunters may have driven small groups of animals into narrow coulees or man-made enclosures to make it easier to slaughter them.

Humans gradually developed new weapons capable of killing at longer range. About 8,000 years ago, Saskatchewan hunters acquired the technique of using an atlatl, a piece of wood with a hooked end which effectively extends the length of a thrower's arm and thus increases his leverage. With an atlatl, a hunter could hurl a stone-tipped dart-like projectile farther and with much more force than with just his arm alone. The atlatl and dart became the preferred weapons for Saskatchewan bison hunters and held that position for about six thousand years.

The first buffalo hunts probably consisted of a group of hunters with spears confronting a lone animal.

As the find at Prelate seems to indicate, hunters also changed hunting techniques to suit a more wary prey. Instead of confronting a lone animal with spears, plains hunters used knowledge of bison behavior to funnel groups of animals into natural traps or man-made enclosures known as pounds. By 5,500 years ago, they were driving bison over cliffs.

About two thousand years ago, hunting technology took a huge leap forward when bows and arrows appeared, apparently coming to the Saskatchewan area from the west. For a few hundred years, hunters continued to use atlatls as well but the older weapon eventually fell out of favor. The next big change in hunting methods came with the

Cattle looking for a good place to have a rub have worn paths around these glacial erratics in a sand hills pasture. Bison used stones like this for the same purpose.

16

reintroduction of horses to North America by the Europeans. By the mid-1800s, native peoples did nearly all their bison hunting on horseback. At first they used lances, but soon progressed to bows and arrows and, when they became available, eventually switched to firearms. But the coming of the Europeans and the introduction of firearms would lead to the end of the bison hunting culture—and almost of the bison itself. The world of the prairie grasslands would be dramatically altered. And during that bitter time of forced change, as they watched their people's way of life coming to an end, two remarkable men met in the Great Sand Hills and pledged peace.

Breaking an Ancient Circle

In the spring of 1876 in the United States, the conflict between native peoples and those pushing into their lands was building to an explosive climax. Many native peoples considered the Black Hills of South Dakota a sacred area and the land had been placed off-limits to white settlers as part of the Fort Laramie Treaty of 1868. Despite this, prospectors began pouring into the area after an 1874 expedition led by George A. Custer confirmed that gold had been discovered there. The Sioux were not going to give up their land without a fight. In late May, 1876, about a month before the Battle of the Little Big Horn, the Sioux Chief Sitting Bull sent a messenger with a gift of tobacco to seek an alliance with Blackfoot Chief Crowfoot. The two groups were traditionally enemies but, the messenger said, if Crowfoot would help Sitting Bull to defeat the U.S. Cavalry, Sitting Bull would then bring his forces to bear on the North West Mounted Police (NWMP) in Blackfoot territory. According to the account given by Hugh Dempsey in *Crowfoot*, the Blackfoot chief rejected the offer, threats were exchanged, and finally Crowfoot promised to ally himself with the NWMP *against* the Sioux if they came to Canada. But when Sitting Bull and his people fled to Canada after the Little Big Horn, Crowfoot took no action against them, perhaps because he knew they came seeking refuge not war. By March of 1877, the last batch of stragglers had crossed into Canada, joining the rest of the Sioux who had set up camps between Cypress Hills and Wood Mountain.

The bison herds were becoming increasingly smaller and harder to find. By the mid-1800s, bison were already suffering from drought and competing with growing herds of cattle and wild horses for grass and water. Hunting for meat by both native and white people increased as populations grew and firearms made the killing much easier. The scale of slaughter increased rapidly as huge numbers of bison were killed to feed railroad track-laying crews, to obtain meat for sale, to open range space for cattle, and, perhaps most of all, to supply hides for a variety of uses including buffalo robes and belts to drive factory machines. Finally, the United States Army embarked on a deliberate policy of wiping out the bison to starve the still-resisting native Plains peoples into submission. By the time Crowfoot led his people on the traditional spring hunt in 1877, the Blackfoot had to travel east nearly to Cypress Hills before locating the herds.

During that bitter time of forced change, as they watched their people's way of life coming to an end, two remarkable men met in the Great Sand Hills and pledged peace.

The bison had drawn others to the area as well, including the Cree and Assiniboine, but they were camped quite a distance to the east. Crowfoot was more concerned about friction with the Sioux, who were uncomfortably close by. He kept tight control on his men, stopping them from raiding the Sioux camps. Sitting Bull knew that if trouble flared up between the Blackfoot and Sioux, his people would probably be forced from Canada. In an overture of friendship and peace, the Sioux chief sent a messenger bearing tobacco and other gifts to Crowfoot. Crowfoot accepted the gifts but remained unsure of Sitting Bull's intentions.

The brown-headed cowbird followed the bison herds, feeding on the insects they stirred up. The cowbird was free to move along because it is a brood parasite, laying its eggs in the nests of other birds. The foster parents raise the young cowbirds as well as their own chicks.

Some time later, when Crowfoot was camped in the Great Sand Hills, word came that another party of Sioux was approaching. This time Sitting Bull himself came, seeking a meeting with Crowfoot. The two men exchanged gifts of tobacco, brought out pipes and had a long conversation. Their talk led to a great friendship, each man respecting and trusting the other. Sitting Bull would eventually give his favorite son the name Crowfoot to honor the Blackfoot chief. Before the Sioux left the Great Sand Hills to return to their own camp, they took part in a friendship dance with the Blackfoot to celebrate peace between their peoples. This was probably one of the last happy times for either of the two great chiefs.

In 1881, after struggling without success to meet the needs of his people in a nearly bison-less world, Sitting Bull surrendered at Fort Buford, Montana. He was shuffled from place to place by the government, which feared his influence with his people, spending his last years on the Standing Rock Reservation in South Dakota. In the early morning hours of December 15, 1890, during a gunfight stemming from the

When a person died, the Blackfoot believed, his soul travelled to the Sand Hills on the eastern edge of their hunting grounds, joining those who had gone before. There the spirits dwelt in phantom villages and pursed ghost buffalo in shadowy replication of their former life.

government's efforts to suppress the Ghost Dance movement, a policeman's bullet ended Sitting Bull's life.

Not long after the meeting in the Great Sand Hills, Crowfoot, knowing that soon the bison would be gone and his people would have to rely on the white men for help, agreed to consider treaty terms being offered by Canadian officials. On September 22, 1877, after a lengthy and complex process of negotiations and consultations, Crowfoot, along with other representatives of the Blackfeet, Blood, Piegan, Sarcee, and Stony peoples, signed Treaty 7. He believed he was securing protection for his people in a rapidly disintegrating world.

Instead, Crowfoot watched his people lose their culture and their identity, becoming strangers in the land that had been their home. In early April 1890, after a long period of ill-health, Crowfoot began preparing himself for one last journey. On April 25, 1890, Crowfoot's spirit started on its way to the Great Sand Hills.

The Blackfoot believed that, in the Great Sand Hills, the dead lived on in shadowy villages. They rode ghostly horses, hunted phantom buffalo, and used possessions that were with them when they died or that were placed with their bodies after death. Ghosts sometimes lingered before completing their journey from one existence to the next. The spirits of those who died horribly or unexpectedly might linger, refusing to accept the fact that they no longer were part of this world. Others might stay to watch over their families. But eventually, they, too, travelled to the Big Sands.

Several stories told of hunting or warring parties unknowingly making camp near or in the Great Sand Hills. During the night, the men heard voices calling and singing, dogs barking, and other sounds of camp life but they could see nothing. In some stories, they heard the voice of a chief telling his people to leave the visitors alone. The men realized they had stumbled into a land of ghosts and the mysterious sounds they heard were supernatural. Terrified, they rolled themselves more tightly in their robes and wished for morning to come. When dawn eventually broke, the noises died away and the men hurriedly continued on their way.

Another Blackfoot tale of the Great Sand Hills, as related by Jim White Bull of the Blood people and recorded by Hugh Dempsey in *The Vengeful Wife and Other Blackfoot Stories*, tells the story of the ghost medicine-pipe bundle and how it came from the land of the dead. Here is a retelling of that story:

A young man whose wife had died decided to go to the Sand Hills and bring her back. Leaving his children with their grandparents, he journeyed east until he entered the hills. A shadow boy, learning what the young man wanted, led him to a tepee. Directed by a voice to take a seat, the young man watched a shadowy figure pick up, light and begin to smoke a pipe. The pipe was passed to other spirits and all became more visible as they smoked. Learning of the young man's quest, the ghost chief offered to take him to the four ghost villages that lay in the Sand Hills. There the young man would be able to look at the women recently arrived from the west to see if he could find his wife. The ghost chief and the young man went to the first three villages with no success but at the fourth village, the grieving husband finally found his wife. The spirit woman smiled and wished to kiss her husband but the chief told her to wait.

Leading the young Blackfoot into a lodge, the ghost chief took down a pipe and said that he was going to transfer the ownership of the pipe to the man, teaching him the songs and ceremonies that went with it. The ghost chief and his friends performed the transfer ritual, telling the man to take the pipe and use its powers to help his people. The ghosts wrapped the pipe, along with a crow-feather fan, a wooden bowl, and a rawhide container, in an owl skin decorated with beaver claws and eagle feathers. The ghost chief called to the young wife, beckoning her into the lodge, where sweet pine smoke was blown over her and the pipe bundle to purify them. The chief secured the pipe bundle to the wife's back with a strap and everyone went outside. The chief told the young Blackfoot that his wife would follow him back to the land of the living. He must never look back at her or speak to her, and he must always face west even when he was sleeping. When he arrived home, he was to perform a set of ritual sweat ceremonies that would cleanse him from his journey with death. If he followed all of these instructions, his wife would be returned to him and with her would come the pipe bundle. The young man did as he was told, regained his wife, and used the power of the pipe to assist his people in times of trouble.

The ghost-medicine pipe was passed down through eight other owners ending with Red Old Man, who died in the 1860s. Upon his death, both of his brothers were offered the pipe but were afraid to take it. The people decided to place the pipe alongside Red Old Man's body so that his spirit could carry it back to the Great Sand Hills.

By the time Crowfoot died in 1890, the bison his people had followed for generations were gone and the Blackfoot themselves were confined at the western edge of their former lands. But in the east, the Blackfoot believed, the spirits of those who had gone before continued their ghostly hunts in the Great Sand Hills, untouched and untouchable by the forces that had turned the world of the Plains peoples upside down.

Exterminating the bison had ecological consequences as well as cultural ones. When explorer John Palliser camped near Moose Jaw Creek in 1858, he saw buffalo across "the whole region, as far as the eye could reach." Great herds of hefty beasts left hard-packed paths across the semi-arid plains. The effect of their prodigious appetites left the grass close-cropped and what the bison didn't eat, they trampled. When they crowded together in small bluffs of trees to get out of the baking sun, their hooves crushed the undergrowth into oblivion. They rubbed against the bigger trees, uprooted seedlings and through all these actions played a role in keeping trees from invading the grasslands.

By the time Crowfoot died in 1890, the bison his people had followed for generations were gone and the Blackfoot themselves were confined at the western edge of their former lands.

Buffalo wallows—shallow pits about 60 cm deep and 3-6 meters across—left the landscape looking, as author Barry Potyondi describes it, "not unlike a golf course with closely spaced sand traps." Wallows could be wet or dry and the bison seemed to use the wet ones to keep cool or avoid bugs, while rolling in the dry wallows may have helped rid itchy animals of their shedding winter coats. Wherever bison cleared away the vegetation, erosion accelerated.

Bison made a big mess of any waterhole they used. Imagine a vast number of large animals tramping through the mud, standing in the water to rid themselves of flies, and excreting urine and feces whenever and wherever the spirit moved them.

Explorers reported water holes filled with more urine than water. Buffalo dung left behind by the passing herds blanketed the prairies, providing a natural supply of fertilizer for the vegetation. On the treeless plains, dried dung—buffalo chips—provided a crucial source of fuel for cooking or staying warm.

We can't know exactly how the grassland ecosystems would have re-stabilized after the bison disappeared. The grass that once fed the great herds and the land that produced it attracted an inflow of people who would reshape the prairies to serve their needs, creating one of the most heavily altered landscapes on Earth.

Broken Land, Broken Dreams

Cattle ranchers were the first to take advantage of the open grasslands of southern Saskatchewan. Spurred by increased global demand for beef following the 1869 herd-reducing anthrax outbreak in Britain, interest in southern Saskatchewan as grazing land jumped when completion of the Canadian Pacific Railroad through the area in 1883 offered an efficient way to move meat to market. An amendment to the Dominion Lands Act in 1881 encouraged large-scale operations by allowing investors to obtain long-term grazing leases on up to 100,000 acres for one cent per acre annually. Quite a few of the big ranches were backed with British money while others were expansions of American operations in Montana. The hardy Longhorn cattle the ranchers chose were tough, but prairie fires and blizzards took their toll.

Blizzards were a particularly serious problem for the early ranchers, who didn't cut and store hay for winter feeding. They expected the cattle to be able to forage for themselves. The first big blizzards hit in the winter of 1886-1887 and thousands of cattle died, often struggling in drifts or trapped in coulees. Other tough winters followed, but the winter of 1906-07—the one responsible for Wallace Stegner's "carrion spring"—marked the end of the vast cattle operations in western Canada. From early fall onwards, storm after storm pelted the prairies. By the time spring arrived, the Turkey Track Ranch near Wood Mountain had lost 18,000 cattle—enough to fold the operation. Losses were even higher than they might have been in previous years because cattle could no longer wander freely to seek food or shelter. Carcasses piled up along the fences that marked out the territory of the newest arrivals to the grasslands—the homesteaders and settlers.

A weathered outhouse huddles forlornly among the sage as an autumn snowstorm swirls through the Sand Hills.

Abandoned buildings and other reminders of left-behind dreams are scattered throughout the Great Sand Hills. Simple crosses (left) arise from the prairie grasses at the abandoned town of Rastad.

The Dominion Lands Act of 1872 made every adult male an attractive offer: for ten dollars he could have 160 acres of farm land—a quarter section. The homesteader promised to prove out his claim by breaking the sod, building a shelter, and living on his property for at least six months per year for three years. Then it was his.

Although there was an immediate land rush and rampant speculation, the government didn't get the influx of farmers that it wanted. Part of the problem was few wished to attempt such a venture in Palliser's Triangle—the area explorer John Palliser described in the late 1850s as having neither arable soil nor enough moisture for agriculture. So, in 1896, the government began an aggressive overseas advertising campaign which portrayed the area in glowing terms.

Minister of the Interior Clifford Sifton wanted settlers who could adapt to the hardships that they would face and targeted the poor farming people of eastern Europe as well as potential settlers in Great Britain. Even eastern Canada heard about this new land of opportunity. Hired speakers, paid journalists, posters, pamphlets—all promised a new life on free land in the "last best west." They spoke of an invigorating climate, but skimmed over the reality of prairie winters. They offered something for the landless, the poor, and the adventurers. And thousands upon thousands of people came.

In the early 1900s, Saskatchewan led Canada in agricultural settlement. In 1908, the Dominion Lands Act was amended to encourage agricultural settlement in less arable areas of the prairies by offering the homesteader an option on a second quarter of land with the payment of an additional ten dollars, and by making other changes amenable to larger family farms. This encouraged a new wave of homesteaders who had to make do with the less desirable land not already under claim. Many had little or no idea what they were getting into. The train took those headed for the area around the Great Sand Hills as far as Moose Jaw to register their claim at the land office, and then on to Gull Lake or Maple Creek. But from there they stepped off the map.

Zoeth F. Cushing built his homestead shack about halfway between the present towns of Hazlet and Cabri. His remembrances of his early years are related with good humor but the realities of what it was like come through clearly. The prairies were a shock for a Nova Scotia boy who ended up on a train to Moose Jaw as the result of a dare. Cushing wrote:

In October 1909, I built my homestead shack on the N.W. 1/4 of Sec. 36 Tp 17 Rg 19. This was the first sign of settlement in what is known today as the Roseray

Urged on by government, homesteaders flocked to Palliser's Triangle. At first the land produced rich harvests of wheat. But the plows that broke the soil exposed the land to the seemingly ceaseless wind, setting the stage for disaster. (Photo upper left: Saskatchewan Archives Board R-A15077)

"In 1930 there was a good crop but in 1931 it was very poor. Dust storms began, it got so bad even the Russian thistles wouldn't grow…The winters were very severe, especially 1934. Many families had to go on relief but it was not sufficient…" — Jacob Helfrich

District. At that time my nearest neighbour was the R.R. Pearce family, six miles Northwest, and my nearest Post Office was Gull Lake, thirty miles distant.

I came to Gull Lake by train, bought enough lumber and nails to build a 12' X 14' shack, and enough grub to last all winter, I thought (but it was really all gone in two weeks.) I got a stove and the necessary equipment to get along with, hired a man with a team and loaded up my lumber, groceries and a few sacks of coal, and started out to find the homestead, which I knew to be about thirty miles North of Gull Lake, and sure hoped I could find it.

We found the S.W. corner of my land on a Sunday afternoon, I don't remember the date but I know it was in October. I will never forget the completely lost feeling I had as I stood there alongside all my worldly possessions on the bald-headed prairie and watched that team disappear through the hills. I was twenty years young, a green kid from the East, in the wilds of Saskatchewan and very much alone…

Alone —and with virtually none of the things that we consider essential to our daily lives. But Cushing was determined to make it, despite the weather that greeted him on his second day.

When I woke the next morning, it was raining and plenty cold. I was quite comfortable under the blankets, but there didn't seem to be much future in that and the idea of getting out wasn't so good. However, I finally decided that I had better get out and get going, I had a home to build and there was no one but myself to do it. What a mess I found, everything soaked and no place to dry anything. I did the only thing I could think of—I started to dig—and by night I had a hole big enough to get all my stuff into. I set up my stove and covered the hole with lumber. There wasn't much room in that hole, but I kept quite comfortable. It had stopped raining and I felt that I had things pretty well under control. The next morning I started to build my home, the hole which I had been living in, I used for a cellar.

I worked at that shack for about two weeks and the only living thing I saw during that time was a gopher, the most appreciated friend I have ever had. He was a cocky little devil and I came to think a lot of him. It is quite likely that in the years ahead, I poisoned and murdered in various ways hundreds of his offspring, but if anyone had tried to harm that gopher at that time, he would have had me to deal with.

Rich in game species like these mule deer, the Sand Hills provided food for homesteaders. Today, sport hunters enjoy the bounty.

After completing my shack, the question arose "What was I to do all winter?" The more I looked at it, the less attractive it seemed. My grub and fuel were gone. My nearest neighbour was six miles and the nearest source of fuel supply, the sand hills about twenty miles away. I had no means of transportation and I knew that my gopher friend would soon hibernate and I would have no company.

The Great Sand Hills, although not actively homesteaded themselves, were mentioned in nearly every local homesteader's account consulted for this book as the source of wood for fuel. In the sea of grass, the shrubs and trees of the area were a valuable resource. For example, Cushing decided to spend his first Saskatchewan winter "batching" with two friends of his from back East, Mert and Frank Freeman, who were homesteading about three miles south of where the town of Abbey stands today. One of the advantages of staying with the Freemans, Cushing relates, is that they lived only about twelve miles from the sand hills, so fuel was no problem.

The Sand Hills were also a choice hunting spot, particularly in winter, when game took shelter there. Once again, Zoeth Cushing tells a good story:

Between Christmas and New Years, Frank and I decided to spend a few days in the sand hills to try and get some prairie chickens and, if lucky, an antelope. The first day we arrived there, pitched our tent and got established for living. About ten o'clock the following morning, I took a gun and started out in search of prairie chicken for dinner. I was only gone about half an hour, when one of our darn fool blizzards came up. I don't remember ever seeing a storm blow up as quickly as that one did. In a matter of minutes, I couldn't see a hundred feet ahead. I knew that I had been travelling West and also that the storm was coming from the West, so I put the storm in my back and started back, hoping that I would be lucky enough to find the tent — a slim chance. I carried on until I realized that I was leaving the sand hills, so turned and faced the storm until I found a clump of willows, good and thick. I was still clutching the prairie chicken I had managed to get and together we crawled into the bluff which was thick enough to give pretty good shelter. Then I broke off some dry willows and piled them up, by dark I had quite a bit of firewood. Fortunately I had matches, so I was pretty well fixed for the night. I got a good fire going and things looked fairly cheerful. My big fight was to keep awake. I was getting pretty hungry too, and all I had to eat was one prairie chicken. About midnight, I couldn't stand it any longer, so I peeled the feathers off the bird and held him over the fire until he was nicely smoked and roasted a little.

If I'd just had a little salt, that bird would have tasted pretty good, as it was I still appreciated him. After midnight, sleep got to be a real problem. I had to keep moving most of the time, if I went to sleep I knew I was finished. About 3 a.m. it started to clear. By 6 o'clock I took my course by the moon and started East. I knew I would never find the tent and my best bet was to get out of the hills, hoping to find a homesteader's shack. I saw a week shack with smoke curling up from it. This looked pretty good to me. I reached the shack about nine-thirty that morning to find two bachelors living there, the Grayson brothers. They are both gone now, but they lived in that same location until a few years ago. I can safely say that they could boil the best beans I have ever tasted. They had about a gallon of them and I sure cleaned them up fast — the first square meal I had had in over twenty-four hours.

I tried to explain to them where the tent was, but it was pretty hard to make much sense to it. However, they had been there quite a while and knew the hills pretty well. They had a team of horses so we set out to look for the tent and were lucky enough to come across it about the middle of the afternoon. Frank had left, taking the bulls, but he had left lots of grub and blankets. I knew that both Frank and Mert would be worrying about me, but I just couldn't force myself to walk that twelve miles without some sleep, so I cooked a good supper for myself, rolled up in my blankets and went to sleep. I had intended to rest only a few hours and then start for home when it was good moonlight. The result was that I slept around the clock and by the time I got breakfast, it was daylight when I started for home. Just as I was getting out of the hills, I met a crowd coming, a whole sleigh load of them. I didn't know there were that many people in the country. They were armed with all the equipment it would be possible to use in digging a man out of the snow — they even had a bottle of Whisky, though where they got that I never knew. When they found that I was safe and sound and in one piece, the only thing to show for it were two frozen toes and one prairie chicken, which I had consumed for my New Year's Eve midnight supper.... Every New Year's Eve since that time, I always think of 1909, when I watched the old year out and the New Year in, in a clump of willows in the sand hills.

In the early years, prairie fires were a constant fear. One of the first tasks of a homesteader when he began breaking land was to plow a firebreak, as Cushing explains:

I started breaking in early March, [1910] a full fledged farmer at last. The first thing I did was to plow a fire guard around my East quarter. This was very important, as one match is all that was needed and thousands of square miles of prairie would go up in smoke, and I was depending on that prairie grass for feed. In fact, that was all the feed I had. That bit of grass growing on the prairie was just as important to me as tractor fuel is to the farmer today.

One day late in March I saw black smoke in the west and I knew a fire was coming. It hit my fireguard about midnight and the guard held. It was a wonderful sight, a solid wall of fire as far as one could see. The whole country was a black waste, all except the quarter section of grass that I had saved. Looking at that quarter section of grassland from a distance, it resembled the size of a postage stamp.

As relentlessly as any fire, a wave of change driven by the dreams of homesteaders swept across the prairies. Across the land, men and teams swept back and forth carving out new lives and new fields.

In 1910 a fire, possibly the same one Cushing describes, burned most of the grass between what are now Cabri and Shackelton. Once a fire started, the nearly ceaseless wind pushed it onward and, on the open plains, there was little to stop it.

As relentlessly as any fire, a wave of change driven by the dreams of homesteaders swept across the prairies. Across the land, men and teams swept back and forth carving out new lives and new fields. The countless plows that bit into the tough sod were literally breaking the land, severing plant roots that held the fragile soil against the tug of the wind. The long-term effects of this large-scale disruption were masked by several years in which the sun and rain were benevolent and the soil poured forth prosperity.

In 1896, 1.26 million acres were planted in wheat. That nearly doubled by 1901 and, by 1913, the total reached more than 10 million acres. Crop yields followed the same trend: 63 million bushels in 1901 soared to 209 million bushels in 1913. By the 1920s, wheat made up one-quarter of Canadian exports by value.

The first hints of the coming catastrophe appeared in southern Alberta, where the drying winds of the Chinook ate away at the broken land. Before long, other areas were experiencing the same problem. Erosion was exacerbated across the prairie by the then standard dryland farming practice of summerfallowing—leaving land without plant growth for an annual growing cycle to store up moisture and nutrients for the next

Open dunes are the most dramatic feature of the Great Sand Hills but make up less than 0.5% of the area. Rugged brush and pasture land, containing a great diversity of plant and animal species, are much more typical.

37

year. Prairie farmers at this time used black fallow summerfallowing, meaning they tilled the ground several times during the growing season to kill weeds and volunteer plants. Each tilling dried out the rich surface soil, leaving it at the mercy of the wind. By 1914, drifts of soil blanketed several areas.

It was the demands of war that really brought the prairie farmers and their land to the brink of disaster. From the day war was declared in August, 1914, the Canadian Government pressured farmers to bring more land under cultivation and to produce more grain. The next year, 4,800,000 more acres were being farmed than the year before. The pressure didn't let up until the war ended in 1918, by which time 12,000,000 acres had been added to pre-war cultivation—more than 5,500,000 of that in the Palliser Triangle alone. As many knowledgeable observers have written, most of that land should never have been broken. That would become abundantly clear when, not too far down the road, the sun and rain stopped being kind.

A series of droughts followed on the heels of a global depression that saw the price of a bushel of wheat drop from $1.27 in 1927 to $0.30 in 1932. Even though the situation became desperate in some areas, people stayed on their farms because there was really nowhere else to go. And as they watched their hopes blow away with the soil, the farmers suffered one natural disaster after another.

Plagues of grasshoppers came from the south in numbers beyond description. Many accounts describe how they ate everything in sight including handles on pitchforks and clothes hanging on the line. The sight of them crawling everywhere and the sound of them chewing must have driven some people to the brink of insanity. In 1933 alone, grasshoppers destroyed more than $30,000,000 of crops. Besides the financial consequences, the loss struck a devastating blow to the farmers' morale. Rain had finally come that spring and the crop looked good until the swarms arrived. Despite well-organized campaigns using tonnes of poison bait, grasshoppers remained a scourge on the prairies until well into the war years when shifting environmental conditions and improved farming practices brought them under control once again.

Besides grasshoppers, the 1930s brought hail, wheat stem rust, sawfly, wireworm, and equine sleeping sickness. Time after time, the crop would look promising only to fall under a natural onslaught. In *Men Against The Desert*, James Gray wrote, "The cloud of discouragement hung heaviest over Saskatchewan, for the very simple reason that in season and out, Saskatchewan had it worst on all counts—worst drouth [sic], worst grasshoppers, worst rust, worst cutworms, worst hail."

Grasshoppers, cutworm, rust, hail, drought—Saskatchewan farmers were driven to despair during the 1930s. Some left their farms or took their own lives. Others struggled on waiting for "normal" life to return.

In 1938, for example, Saskatchewan farmers planted nearly their entire crop from relief seed provided by the government and things started off well. Then came the grasshoppers from the south and, when their attack was at its peak, a near epidemic of wheat stem rust in July. This was followed by severe hailstorms coupled with the depredations of a peak crop of wireworms. Reading the daily accounts of those times leaves an impression of the prairie farmer as a blindfolded man battered to his knees, wondering from where the next blow will come, and yet still struggling somehow to rise again. Not all continued to struggle. The census of 1936, when worse was still to come, reported that 8,200 farms had been abandoned in Saskatchewan.

Those that stayed fought a constant battle with the blowing soil. Mae Seaman, who grew up north of the Great Sand Hills in Prelate, reminisced:

> *How well I remember the dark black clouds rising from the horizon, soon everything was enveloped in a cloud of dust. We often couldn't see the school across the road from us. By 9:00 or 10:00 a.m. it was already dark in the homes and lights burned all day. The dust sifted in all the windows and door frames, as they were all parched and shrunken from no rains for several years.*

The farmers would dampen large size handkerchiefs and put them over their nose and mouth to try and screen out the dust. People were constantly having to wash their hair as it was "loaded"....

Gardens and crops were blown out or buried in sand year after year. The only water the few plants that survived in the garden got was what was hauled several blocks by the pailfuls from the town well. What an oasis that well was!!...

The farmers weren't completely on their own in their battle for survival. The Dominion Experimental Farm system, established in 1886, had been accumulating information on crops, farming practices, and pest control since its inception. From the experimental farms on the prairies came practical advice, organization, and helping hands. And in 1935 from the Experimental Farms came the people and ideas behind perhaps the most practical, forward-thinking solution ever to emerge from a government organization: the Prairie Farm Rehabilitation Administration (PFRA).

The first step toward stopping the blowing dirt seemed obvious: take unsuitable land out of production and get it covered with vegetation. A tangled knot of legal

Looking like a relic of earlier ranching days, a longhorn steer stands in the morning mist on the Bowie ranch near Piapot. He serves as leader for a herd of cows and calves which follow him to and from pasture.

complexities, overlapping federal and provincial jurisdictions, and land titles on abandoned lands made the kind of rapid action that was needed on this issue seem impossible. The PFRA, run by the federal government because they were the only ones with enough money, was an attempt to slice through the red tape and do what needed to be done. The details of the many PFRA programs make fascinating reading and could fill several books by themselves. However, one program in particular—the community pastures program, which got underway in 1937—has had a long-lasting effect in the Great Sand Hills.

PFRA agents purchased marginal land from either individual owners or from municipalities that had reclaimed the title for back taxes. The land was then turned back to pasture, which was then available for lease by local stockmen. In addition to the federal program, Saskatchewan developed its own complementary community pastures program. (Interestingly, Alberta never took part in the PFRA, refusing to return recently acquired responsibility for their natural resources to the federal government. They established their own community pastures instead.)

Land purchase by the PFRA offered many a way out of an impossible situation— trapped in debt on unfarmable land—and allowed them to leave with dignity. The program also provided badly needed employment for many building the miles of new fences the pastures required. In some areas, the PFRA also financed construction of dugouts and stock dams.

The first step toward stopping the blowing dirt seemed obvious: take unsuitable land out of production and get it covered with vegetation.

Buying the land was the easy part. Getting something desirable to grow on it was more difficult. In the drought-stricken prairies, very few types of seed would germinate and survive. Tough annual and perennial weeds did establish a foothold, providing fierce competition for any available moisture and so making it unlikely that native grasses would re-establish themselves. Experimental Farm researchers found the answer in a Siberian import called crested wheatgrass (*Agropyron cristatum*). Resistant to fire, drought, cold temperatures, and heavy grazing, crested wheatgrass proved invaluable in stabilizing the soil. Farmers also grew the plant for seed, earning income as they provided others with the means to combat erosion. Today, crested wheatgrass is sometimes considered an invasive weed and, as such, a threat to native prairie grasses but it played a vital role in putting an end to the rolling clouds of dust.

When the Dust Stopped Blowing

The community pastures programs made much of the land in Palliser's Triangle productive again. In the Great Sand Hills area, the people that had stuck it out gained the use of good grazing land without the financial burden of ownership. Instead, they paid pasture lease fees, which were set just high enough to provide enough money for maintaining fences, hiring a manager to oversee grazing, and paying everyday expenses. This system meant that ranchers could expand their herds and farmers could add livestock to their operation, allowing them to hedge their bets against poor crops. As with any industry there would be growing pains—instances of over-grazing, problems with water supply—but these new grazing operations would find their own equilibria with the Sand Hills landscape, just as surviving older ones had. It was simply a matter of necessity: manage your main resource (grass) well or you will have no way to make an income. As you will see shortly, some of these businesses have worked out a relationship with the Sand Hills ecosystem that has allowed them to survive successfully for decades.

Even during the tough times, the Great Sand Hills had continued to be a place of enjoyment for people living nearby. Sometimes they offered temporary respite from worry. Helen E. Alexander wrote, in her memories of the years 1920-1942:

> I remember hunting the cows in early morning over the hills, sometimes in the rain. Yes, there were seasons when it rained. The hills were beautiful and the bird songs an inspiration, a delightful experience. We often watched the Prairie Chicken Dance together. One day we drove over a sand hill with democrat [wagon] and team, right into a Dance, and we stopped. The chickens went right on dancing, never noticing us.

Some Sand Hills traditions continued from homestead times right through the Depression to the present day. Many accounts speak of church picnics and other gatherings in the hills. Foot races up the steep dune faces were popular and one can only imagine the laughing and shouting that accompanied them. Expeditions to pick Saskatoon berries and chokecherries were also popular. Alexander remembered:

Intricate iron work forms the markers in the Rastad cemetery. Now a ghost town, Rastad was large enough to have its own post office from 1913 until 1932. Many other Sand Hills communities followed the same pattern, springing to life in a surge of optimism then fading away as years of drought and crop failures wore them down.

…Sometimes three or four families went on picnics to the sandhills, and everyone somersaulted down the sand bar. Remember the tiger-lilies and the yellow ladie's [sic] slippers? We picniced [sic] in the sandhills in cherry-blossom time and we picniced [sic] in cherry-picking time.…

Sometimes several families went together in a wagon to pick chokecherries. We took tubs and boilers, water pails and lard pails to fill. Those cherries were delicious. In dry years they were big and juicy, a treat to eat right off the trees and Nature's own tonic through the winter. We made syrup and jelly, preserved them with the pits, and, mind you, Mother and I sat up till midnight pitting them by hand, then bottling them in cherry syrup, for a special treat.

Abundant crops of chokecherries drew homesteaders into the Sand Hills for picking parties.

Despite their many attractions, the Great Sand Hills were not choice land for the homesteader. There was good drinkable water there, near the surface, but no way to farm the land. So the Great Sand Hills sat wrapped in their thin green coverlet, through the homestead era, the Depression and the dust bowl, remaining mostly untouched by the events around them. But there were some points of contact.

What became of these towns? Perhaps their people lost men in the Great War, or they lost one too many crops, or maybe they just lost heart.

In a small, gray book in the Saskatchewan Archives Board is a list of post offices with the dates they were established and the dates they closed. Making a list of those located in the Great Sand Hills area, I stumbled across names I couldn't find on the map: Avonhill (1915-1923), Baxterville (1913-1922), Caesarville (1911-1914), Elardee (1913-1929), Gallon (1913-1914), Georgina (1910-1914), Golden Rule (1924-1927), Graydahl (1915-1927), Harnett (1912-1918), Invernairn (1910-1917), Lobethal (1905-1912), Longworth (1910-1912), Rastad (1913-1932), Skibereen (1900-1927), Wapashoe (1912-1931). What became of these towns? Perhaps their people lost men in the Great War, or they lost one too many crops, or maybe they just lost heart. Like fireflies, these places were born, burned brightly for a short time, and then just flickered out. The homestead era, Depression, and "dirty '30s" took place less than a hundred years ago and yet, for most of us, it's "history"—that dry stuff that happened to someone else a long time ago. But in the Great Sand Hills, "history" may be only two generations away. Interest and memories are strong. And so is pride in the Sand Hills as they are today.

The Present

When I first visited the Great Sand Hills, I was impressed with the size of the dunes but what really took my breath away was the sheer abundance of life in what I had imagined as a barren place. Just for fun, I made a list of the birds and mammals my husband and I saw over a three-day period in early July. The tally reached 7 mammal species and an astonishing 37 bird species, including long-billed curlews, pelicans, and burrowing owls. More than 200 plant species, over 150 bird species and in excess of 40 species of mammals, reptiles, and amphibians live in the Great Sand Hills during part or all of the year. At the end of this book are appendices listing the plant and animal species found in the Great Sand Hills. They are as complete as possible—I was not allowed access to data from the bird and plant surveys completed for the GSHRES— but the names on the page don't capture the vibrant, varied inhabitants and the experience of sharing the landscape with them. Birds singing, insects buzzing, the smell of sun-baked soil and sage . . . everywhere around me was life. Quite a change from the surrounding agricultural areas where wildflowers and wildlife seemed confined to the fence lines and road allowances. As I learned more about the Great Sand Hills, I began to understand why such a wealth of species call this place home.

Climate and Landscape

The image most people have of the Great Sand Hills is of bare sand shaped into sensual curves by the wind. These are the photographs of the area that appear most often in magazines and calendars but, in fact, less than 0.5 percent of the Great Sand Hills is open, active sand. The rest consists of dunes stabilized by a thin vegetative cover, sand sheets, and deflation areas or blowouts. The steep faces of the dunes and the fact that they are close together give the impression of a rugged landscape despite the fact that few individual dunes are more than 15 meters tall.

As those of us who live on the prairies know, the only certain thing about the weather here is its uncertainty. It's not unheard of to run your air conditioning and your heat in the same day. Warm, wet Pacific and dry, cold Arctic air masses interact here, keeping things stirred up, and the rain shadow of the Rocky Mountains plays a part in the scheme of things as well. In general, the Great Sand Hills have cold winters and dry to very dry summers. Rainfall amounts can change dramatically from year to year. When rain does fall, it comes mainly in the rapid downpours of thunderstorms and drains away quickly into the sandy ground. There is no drainage network of streams here—the water isn't around long enough to form one. The amount of moisture lost annually by evapotranspiration—evaporation from the soil and transpiration from plants—is greater than the annual amount of precipitation by an average of about 40 percent. This is thirsty land.

Yet, you can find water here and must, if you wish to raise livestock. Most shallow wells—from about 5 to 100 meters deep—and dugouts in the Sand Hills get their water from near-surface sand and gravel aquifers. Windmills, electric pumps, and solar-powered pumps raise it to the surface. In some places, the water table is close enough to the surface—3 to 6 meters—that a simple sand point well can be driven into the ground. In its simplest form, a sand point is small diameter pipe with a screened open area above a hardened drive point. The screen keeps sand out while allowing water to flow in. Water quality in these near-surface aquifers is usually excellent—fresh to slightly saline—but they may be limited in quantity or flow rate. And, because of their shallow depth, these aquifers are highly susceptible to contamination. The same soil permeability that allows rainwater to quickly disappear in the sand hills allows biological or chemical contaminants to travel rapidly through the aquifers.

This is thirsty land. Yet you can find water here and must, if you wish to raise livestock.

Deeper beneath the Great Sand Hills lie other aquifers composed of layers of sand and gravel with less permeable material between them. For groundwater hydrologists, glacial aquifers can be frustrating, spotty, thick-thin affairs: missing where you expect to find them, interconnected when you think they are separate, or partially plugged up

A smelly, saline crust covers the playa near the Ingebrigt Lake mine.

with intermixed clays. Thus, one report identified three aquifers beneath a portion of the Sand Hills: one less than 25 meters below the surface but with reduced permeability; a second occurring 15 to 100 m below the surface; a third at 100-160 m depth varying in thickness from 5 to 50 meters. Water quality and flow rates vary.

If you go below the glacial deposits, the bedrock aquifers aren't that appealing. The waters they contain often smell and taste bad, and may have a total dissolved solids (TDS) rating greater than that allowed for human consumption. Still, beggars can't be choosers and, in this arid place, some have had to look deep to find water for their cattle.

You can find some water on the surface in the Great Sand Hills but it is usually much more valuable as wildlife habitat than as a consistent water source. The two largest water bodies in the area, Bigstick Lake and Crane Lake, sit on the outskirts of the Sand Hills and receive inflow creeks originating in the Cypress Uplands. When there is enough water, which usually means spring, both wetlands areas are used to supply water for livestock. Bigstick Lake, however, has rather saline water which tends to decrease in both quality and quantity as the summer progresses. Piapot Creek, which originates in the Cypress Uplands, drains into Crane Lake, giving it a more reliable water supply. Despite this, during the drought years of the 1930s, Crane Lake—six miles (9.7 km) long and three miles (4.8 km) wide—went bone dry. In more recent years, Ducks Unlimited built several small dams at the upstream end of Bigstick Lake and a central ring dam at Crane Lake to help maintain a slightly more stable water supply at both locations.

Scattered throughout the Great Sand Hills proper are alkaline lakes or playas. In places such as Ingebrigt Lake, North Ingebrigt Lake, Snakehole Lake and a host of small depressions, malodorous water laps sluggishly at salt-crusted shores. Most of these playas are small, shallow, and seasonal, filling with water in spring and early summer and drying up by summer's end. Their presence is due more to high local water tables than to any surface runoff. During the summer, when evaporation is rapidly sucking water out of the playa basin, shallow groundwater containing dissolved minerals flows upward to replace it. As evaporation begins to exceed inflow, the mineral solution becomes concentrated and eventually precipitates out to form the white crusts visible along the shore. Protected from further evaporation, the mud beneath the crusts stays moist. Along some playa shores, plants and mats of cyanobacteria carpet the mud flats. Cyanobacteria, sometimes called blue-green algae, are an incredibly ancient form of life. In fact, the oldest known fossils in the world are those of cyanobacteria 3.5 billion years old.

A building at the idle Ingebrigt Mine sits next to stockpiled sodium sulphate. (Right) Playas have their own unique ecosystems which include plants able to tolerate the highly alkaline conditions.

Part of the shoreline at 700-acre (280-hectare) Ingebrigt Lake, is a bit different. There, at the end of a dusty gravel road miles from anywhere, one of North America's largest sodium sulphate mines and processing plants sits idle. In 1999, the facility produced just under 140,000 tons of sodium sulphate, which is used in some paper pulping processes and in detergent manufacturing. Operators used a floating dredge to recover the raw minerals from the lake, then cleaned and processed them for shipment as crystalline sodium sulphate. Due to "high energy costs," the Ingebrigt Lake plant has been shut down since the end of 2000, but another sodium sulphate plant at Chaplin, SK, owned by the same company, is still in production.

Dry hilly land, alkaline lakes, an 80°C difference in winter and summer temperatures —what could possibly live here? One of the most intriguing combinations of flora and fauna to be found in North America.

The Plants

When an icy wind comes howling out of the north, we duck around a corner or into a convenient doorway to find some relief. In the middle of a hot summer day, we seek shade. We're looking for a favorable microclimate within the overall environment. Prairie gardeners play the microclimate game with plants all the time. Certain plants will do well on the shady north side of a house, others crave morning light only. A barely hardy rose that would definitely die in an open field may do just fine if you plant it in a sheltered south-facing bed.

Well adapted to dry conditions, the prickly pear cactus soaks up the slightest rainfall with roots that are close to the surface and stores the moisture inside its pad-like stems beneath a waxy skin. The prickly pear's leaves have been reduced to spines which both shade and protect the plant but offer less surface area for moisture to evaporate.

The topography of the Great Sand Hills offers a wide assortment of microclimates, making it possible for a variety of species to survive here. When combined with the often near surface water table, this can make for some unexpected juxtapositions. At one point, I stepped through sage, an arid land plant, to look at some horsetails, usually found on damp, boggy ground. On another occasion, I painfully encountered prickly pear cacti, which like it dry, at the top of a sun-baked slope. I descended the opposite side of the hill to apply antiseptic in the shade of the moisture-loving cottonwoods. On steep, stabilized dunes, it is often possible to see a distinct line where the vegetation changes from a thin cover dominated by grasses and sagebrush (*Artemisia spp.*) on the south-facing slope to a denser one of wild rose (*Rosa woodsii*) and silverberry (*Elaeagnus commutata*) on the north side. Vegetative cover, in turn, creates its own microclimate, shading the soil beneath it and protecting it from some of the wind's drying sting.

A remarkable variety of plant species find agreeable niches in the Great Sand Hills, including this narrow-leaved milk-vetch.

Just a sample of the many plants found in the Great Sand Hills: (clockwise from upper left) small lupine, annual fescue, blue grama, yellow flax.

56

Top: little bluestem.
Bottom left: western red lily.
Bottom right: spiderflower.

On a scorching day in the Sand Hills, the landscape is a subtle blend of metallic hues—the silvery leaves of buffalo berry, the dull glint of golden grass stems, the baked blue-green patina of sage. Even the sky has a hard enamel appearance. With each breath, the richly scented air drags moisture from my lungs and I can feel my skin burning wherever the light touches it. Even when I duck into the shade of some brushy trees, the heat barely lessens. The plants that live here cope much better than I. They are tough, drought-resistant survivors. Prairie grasses also evolved a strategy to survive the fires that often swept the plains until recent times. Burn a tree down, it stays down, but the vital parts of grass plants are underground. They regenerate quickly and soon new green growth emerges from blackened ground. From the time the grasslands appeared, recurring fires removed debris, clearing the way for new growth, and kept trees from spreading into the grasslands.

Grasses once found across the plains, including blue grama grass (*Bouteloua gracilis*), western wheatgrass (*Agropyron smithii*), needle-and-thread grass (*Hesperostipa comata*), are still found in the Great Sand Hills. You know you have truly walked on the prairie when, two hours later, a piece of needle-and-thread grass works its way through your sock to give you a sharp greeting. It seems only fitting that needle-and-thread grass, also known as spear grass, is the official grass of Saskatchewan.

Pincushion cactus blooms with an eye-catching pink. The cacti found in the Great Sand Hills prefer open areas and must tolerate both baking heat and frigid cold.

Another provincial emblem, the western red lily (*Lilium philadelphicum*) lives in the Great Sand Hills as well although it can be shy, especially during very dry years. Other flowers add splashes of color to the predominantly green and tan summer landscape: blazingstars (*Liatris sp.*), wild flax (*Linum lewisii*), purple prairie-clover (*Petalostemon purpureum*), scarlet globemallow (*Sphaeralcea coccinea*), and blanketflower (*Gaillardia aristata*) among others.

Many of the plants found in the Great Sand Hills are widespread and familiar, including Manitoba maple (*Acer negundo*), saskatoon (*Amelanchier alnifolia*), goldenrod (*Solidago spp.*), and cattail (*Typha latifolia*). A host of others, such as six-weeks fescue (*Vulpia octoflora*), beaked annual skeleton-weed (*Shinneroseris rostrata*) and prickly milk-vetch (*Astragalus kentrophyta*), are rare. The Great Sand Hills is one of the few places in western Canada where *Downingia laeta* has been found.

One of the most interesting and valuable aspects of the plant communities found in the Great Sand Hills is the appearance of other habitat types within the general scheme of typical mixed grass prairie. These areas often reflect localized changes in growing condition.

Playas, for example, are home to a unique plant community capable of coping with the soil conditions. Red samphire (*Salicornia rubra*) is so salt-tolerant that it is often found growing alone on the dry lake bottom, where the conditions are simply too harsh for other plants. Near the playa edge, other species, including wild barley (*Hordeum jubatum*), Nuttall's salt-meadow grass (*Puccinellia nuttalliana*) and alkali grass (*Distichlis stricta*) find slightly more agreeable situations.

Damp soils that are less salty, such as those found in some of the sand flats between the dunes, are home to cottonwood (*Populus deltoides*) and river birch (*Betula occidentalis*). Beneath them may grow wild rose, blunt-leaved sandwort (*Arenaria lateriflora*), creeping juniper (*Juniperus horizontalis*), wild licorice (*Glycyrrhiza lepidota*), northern gooseberry (*Ribes oxyacanthoides*) and others.

One of the more disturbing developments in the Great Sand Hills ecosystem is the increasing presence of non-native, or exotic, species that pose a threat because they crowd out native plants. These aggressive newcomers include stinkweed (*Thlaspi arvense*), white sweet clover (*Melilotus alba*), Russian thistle (*Salsola kali*), field bindweed (*Convolvulus arvensis*) and the ubiquitous dandelion (*Taraxacum officinale*). A 2003 inventory of 240 Great Sand Hills sites found that 91% of those sites contained at least one exotic species. Areas where the native vegetative cover has been disturbed, such as along trails and at well sites, provide places for invasive species to gain a foothold. And, as anyone who has tried to remove dandelions or thistles from a lawn will agree, given an inch, these plants will take an acre.

Adding a few new plants to an ecosystem and losing some old ones may not seem so terrible but there are several reasons to be concerned. Each bit of ground lost to an invader means less reproductive chances for native species. Shifts or losses in plant populations can have cascading effects on other parts of the ecosystem, most of them unpredictable. Removing or reducing a food plant, for example, may reduce the population of whatever feeds upon it, which will reduce the food available to the next tier of consumers and so on. Environmental researchers have found that removing even rare species, which make up only a small percentage of the total biomass of the grassland, makes the area more vulnerable to invasion by exotic species. One of the researchers, Erika S. Zavaleta, explained that each species potentially performs different services within an ecosystem. She added, "It turns out that rare things matter a lot."

Even crested wheatgrass, the savior plant of the 1930s, has its drawbacks. In a comparison performed at Grasslands National Park, scientists found that the soil beneath crested wheatgrass contains significantly less organic matter than the soil under native prairie. They believe the discrepancy is related to the growth habits of the plants. Crested wheat puts most of its energy into above ground growth while native prairie plants are shorter but have extensive root systems, which are believed responsible for the favorable soil modifications. In the 1930s, a truly dedicated agricultural scientist added together the length of all the roots on a single four-month old rye grass plant: 620 kilometers or a bit more than the distance from Maple Creek to Moosomin. Roots like that are what made the prairie sod tough enough to use for building houses.

What makes the plant community of the Great Sand Hills so special is the number of species it contains, or its plant biodiversity. Biodiversity has become a popular topic for research and discussion. Since we realized that we're rapidly losing it, everyone is talking about it. The grasslands suffered a dramatic drop in biodiversity when a few agricultural crops replaced the native prairie vegetation. What we lost was the ability to roll with nature's punches.

Biodiversity stabilizes ecosystems. Common sense says this is true—more species mean more of a chance that one will have the characteristics needed to survive in a crisis—and recent discoveries have confirmed it. In an experiment with implications for the production of biofuels, researchers compared multi-species prairie grasslands to single species grasslands. They determined that diverse grasslands produce 240% more biomass than single species grasslands. The diverse areas were also better at withstanding and recovering from long-term stress including climate extremes, pests, and diseases.

Plants in the Great Sand Hills survive searing summers, icy winters, drought, insects, and grazing to form the anchor points of an intricate web. Their roots stabilize the soil, keeping the restless sands from shifting. And, along with the mix of habitats they both occupy and create, the rich variety of plants in the Sand Hills invites an abundance of wildlife.

61

The Animals

Deciding to take a better look at a blowout near the trail one evening, I walked over. Blowouts are deflation features. The wind finds a vulnerable patch of exposed sand—perhaps an animal burrow or a vehicle track—in an otherwise vegetated area. The wind eats away at the weak spot, picking up sand and carrying it away, leaving a depression in the dune. Blowouts can grow to be very large as the edges continue to be undercut and collapse.

This was a good-sized blowout—two or three times my height in depth and maybe 15 meters in diameter. Tracks told me that several children, deer, birds, and some unidentifiable small creatures had been here recently. As I watched, a black beetle came scurrying along with the air of being on a definite mission. The sand in the Great Sand Hills is incredibly fine—I've seen an ant leave tracks—and the trail of the beetle made it clear that he and his kin were responsible for some of the "unknown" tracks criss-crossing the blowout.

From the floor of the blowout, my world was a disc of evening sky with a border fringe of low, bushy shrubs. From one of them, two bare branches extended, the only real elevated point within view. A house wren, tail sassily erect, landed, made a brief statement and fluttered off. He returned about five minutes later and repeated the performance. I picked up my gear, struggled partly up the concave face of the dune below and to the side of his perch, and settled in to watch.

This short, bare stick appeared to be the local equivalent of "Speaker's Corner." Not only did the house wren put in several appearances, but a pair of mountain bluebirds, an eastern kingbird, and several unidentifiable SBB's (small brown birds) took their turn at the perch as well. Swallows swooped into and around the blowout, dining (I hoped) on the plentiful and active mosquito population. A bit later, a chorus of buzzing beeps overhead signaled the arrival of the nighthawk squadron on their regular evening patrol and I made my way back out into the open to watch them.

This kind of experience is not unusual in the Great Sand Hills. There seem to be birds *everywhere* and so many different kinds that the area attracts flocks of birdwatchers. The mix of habitats and lack of human presence make this a unique sanctuary. Rare and threatened species with diverse environmental requirements, such as the piping plover (*Charadrius melodus*), Sprague's pipit (*Anthus spragueii*), and burrowing owl (*Athene cunicularia*) can all find a space that works for them.

63

A drive to the Ingebrigt Mine offered a chance to see a different group of birds than I had observed at the blowout. Fence posts en route provided perches for upland sandpipers, who studied us with large eyes and then resumed preening. These birds seem out of place in the grassland, looking for all the world as though they should be on a beach somewhere. But this is where they breed and raise their chicks because here they can find a mix of habitats that meets their complex requirements. Upland sandpipers want obvious perches in short grass while courting but prefer open, grazed pastures for raising their chicks.

Western meadowlarks are possibly the only birds you can hear singing while zooming past them at 100 kilometers per hour with the windows closed.

Photo: Glen & Rebecca Grambo

Other birds perch along the fences as well, some species preferring the posts and others the wires. Western meadowlarks (*Sturnella neglecta*), possibly the only birds you can hear singing while zooming past them at 100 kilometers per hour with the windows closed, are definite post perchers. They are one of my favorite birds and I was saddened to learn that their numbers have been declining for several years. I cannot imagine a prairie spring without them. The number of bright yellow breasts beaming in the sun as we pass by is reassuring.

The wire sitters include lark buntings (*Calamospiza melanocorys*), which I often describe as "those birds that look like red-winged blackbirds except with white instead of red." At times, groups of them nearly fill the wires between adjacent fence posts. I had heard mourning doves while hiking in the Sand Hills but here I could see them clearly, their sleekly rounded bodies tapering to long, straight tails. The sunlight discovered iridescence concealed in their soft gray feathers. Along with the sleepy buzzing of cicadas, it is the hollow hoo-HOO-hoo-hoo of the mourning dove that I remember from sultry summer afternoons in South Dakota. Hearing them again in the Great Sand Hills made the years fall away.

As we approached the salt plant at Ingebrigt Lake, small playas appeared on either side of the road. Shorebirds skittered here and there, some alone, some in pairs, and a large group navigated through the shallows like a shoal of fish. A pair of avocets seemed a bit skittish, which became understandable when we caught a glimpse of what looked like a spotted cotton ball on toothpick legs. With its chick close behind, underfoot, and sometimes ahead, one of the adults looked for food while keeping to the shallow part of the lake. Sweeping its long curved bill back and forth on the surface of the water, the bird stirred up insects, small crustaceans and other tasty bits, which it then scooped up in its bill.

Farther out in the water, a few birds spun like dervishes first one way, then the other. Phalaropes, I guessed and confirmed it with binoculars. Their distinctive spinning behavior, which had allowed me to identify them, draws water up from beneath them, bringing along deeper-dwelling invertebrates than those the avocets eat. Phalaropes are unusual because, unlike most bird species, females in breeding plumage are more brightly colored than males. This makes sense when you learn that a female phalarope will lay more than one clutch of eggs during a season, each with a different male. Considering each clutch may weigh nearly as much as the female, this is a remarkable biological feat. Incubation and chick-rearing duties are the responsibility of the males. Phalaropes are one of the few birds species known to use this mating strategy, which is known as polyandry.

We left the phalaropes behind and pressed on to the salt plant at the end of the road. Stopping the car to take a look around, we noticed a hawk hunting overhead, low and slow. With a stiff wind blowing, a pair of ferruginous hawks were soaring right over our heads, back and forth between the grassland on our left and the plant buildings on our right. Circle after circle, seeming to adjust course with the slightest deflection of a wingtip, the hawks drifted by. A commotion erupted from a stand of trees near the buildings and a pair of eastern kingbirds began diving at a hawk, pecking at its head. Through the binoculars, and later in photographs, we could see the kingbird actually land on the hawk's back and attack it. The hawk seemed undaunted by the harassment and continued to circle the area. The kingbirds kept up a spirited defense of their territory. We watched for nearly half an hour, not believing our luck in being able to see the hawks so well and to witness their interaction with the kingbirds.

As we left to return the way we had come, I noticed two pelicans in one of the small side pools by the salt mine. Out on the extensive flats, birds were everywhere, going about the business of looking for food. As we passed the playas where we stopped earlier, I saw the avocets with their chick still strolling along the shoreline and the flock of Wilson's phalaropes continued to perform their intricate choreography. I was well satisfied with all I had seen but there were two surprises still to come.

Catching something "not quite right" out of the corner of my eye, I called out to stop the

Male sharp-tailed grouse dispute possession of a prime area of the dancing lek. (Photo: Glen & Rebecca Grambo)

*(Clockwise from upper left)
An American avocet and its
chick stroll along the edge
of a playa. (Photo: Glen &
Rebecca Grambo); a spider
hunts for its next meal; an
eastern kingbird harasses a
ferruginous hawk; a
mountain bluebird perches
near its nest (Photo: Glen
& Rebecca Grambo).*

car and we backed up to take a look. Some "hawk-colored" blotches looked out of place on a slight slope. Binoculars revealed a hawk with three nearly completely fledged chicks sitting on the ground. The adult had apparently brought food and the young ones were eating. We left them to their meal and pressed on. When we were nearly back to the highway, something again caught my eye. In a small tree was a large nest just visible through a gap in the foliage. Using binoculars, I could see chicks in the nest and an adult Swainson's hawk perched next to it. I spend a great deal of time looking for and at wildlife and the chance to see raptors like this is truly a privilege. It is not a common occurrence. But while I was in the Great Sand Hills I saw hawks and other raptors, along with a multitude of other birds. This is a wonderful place for them, and, therefore, for us.

Large numbers of sharp-tailed grouse, Saskatchewan's provincial bird, live in the Great Sand Hills year round. The area is believed to hold one of the largest concentrations of sharp-tails on the Canadian prairies. Each year, sometime between late March and the end of May, depending on the weather, sharp-tails respond to an age-old hormonal call triggered by the increasing hours of daylight. In groups averaging 8 to 12 birds but containing up to 50, the sharp-tails gather at their dancing grounds, or leks. The males are here to impress the females with their dancing and with their position on the lek. The closer to the center of the lek a bird dances, the higher his social status and desirability as a mate. The prime real estate is hotly contested.

It begins just before dawn on frozen ground that will soon be worn bare by the dancing grouse. The females poke about at the edges of the lek, disappearing at times into the grass. The males arrange themselves on the ground and, at some invisible signal, begin to dance. Feet stomping with blurring speed, wings outstretched, heads down, tail feathers up, they race around looking for all the world like small airplanes trying to work up enough speed to take off. They periodically interrupt their mad whirl to cluck and give a soft boom which displays their lavender throat pouch, and then they're off again. As they dance, the males shake their tail feathers, producing a scraping sound as the feathers rub against each other. The noise level is high but, suddenly, all motion and sound stop. Males may face off in pairs, often squatting down in the dirt. These face-offs sometimes lead to short but frantic spur-gouging, wing-beating fights. The dancing begins again, continuing in these spurts until daylight. The sharp-tail dance is a comic display to watch but a stroll across the lek when the birds are gone reveals blood-stained feathers that leave no doubt of the ritual's importance to the grouse.

Other animals share the Sand Hills with the birds. I watched mule deer browse quietly

(Clockwise from upper left) A cedar waxwing perches in sage; a beetle scuttles busily across the fine sand; a speedy pronghorn pauses to look around; Wilson's phalaropes move in formation through the shallows of a playa. (All photos except pronghorn: Glen & Rebecca Grambo)

in the evening, and, on a sweltering afternoon, spied a buck bedded down on the shady side of a hill where he could catch a cooling breeze. There are white-tailed deer here as well, and pronghorns graze on the grasses. The lanky white-tailed jack rabbit and the petite Nuttall's cottontail can each find habitat to their liking but unless you catch them moving, they are difficult to spot. Muskrat, porcupine, badger—each has different environmental needs yet all find accommodation in the Great Sand Hills.

Some of the smaller mammals reveal themselves by the tracks and traces they leave behind. I've never seen a northern pocket gopher in action but judging from the mounds of freshly turned earth they leave nearly everywhere, they must be industrious. I was especially on the lookout for the distinctive tracks of one of the Sand Hills' most well-known yet least-seen inhabitants: Ord's kangaroo rat.

The Great Sand Hills are home to one of the most northern populations of Ord's kangaroo rat. This rare species prefers to live just at the edge of active dune areas. (Photo: David Gummer/Royal Alberta Museum)

Relatively small, with a long brush-tipped tail that makes up more than half of its 10-inch total length, Ord's kangaroo rat is a feisty furball that will aggressively defend its burrows and food caches from intruders. Rather than scurry about on all fours, it hops about on its huge hind feet, using its tail for balance when necessary. The kangaroo rat uses its small front feet for gathering and manipulating food, which includes plant seeds and insects. Active at night, the kangaroo rat collects food, stuffs it into its cheek pouches and carries it back to the burrow. Ord's kangaroo rat prefers to live in sparsely vegetated dune areas. If the dunes become covered and stabilized, the kangaroo rats use less suitable, partially open terrain such as trails, roads, and fallow fields. Although the Great Sand Hills offer perfect habitat for the kangaroos rats, the climate presents an interesting and often insurmountable challenge to their survival.

Most kangaroo rats live in warm climates and remain active throughout the year. Northern populations, such as those in the Great Sand Hills and in southeastern Alberta, must deal with long, cold winters. They store food and cannot continue to forage when there is snow. To make the food last longer, they use a form of shallow hibernation called torpor. They rouse themselves to eat at night and then enter torpor during the day, which slows their body processes. According to researcher David Gummer, only about 1 in 10 kangaroo rats survives a typical Canadian winter. Most simply don't have enough food or energy to make it through until spring. Because there are so few kangaroo rats around in early spring, adds Gummer, it is all the more important that land uses not have a negative impact on those survivors.

Along with the sand dune denizens like the kangaroo rat, the Great Sand Hills is also home to creatures with very different habitat needs. Several species of amphibians, including rare ones such as the Plains spadefoot toad, Great Plains toad, and Northern leopard frog, live here. If you know where and how to look, you might see a tiger salamander or Canadian toad. Once again, it is the unique combination of habitats found in the Great Sand Hills which allows both desert and moisture-loving species to live here.

The Canadian toad (shown here) as well as the much less common Plains spadefoot toad and Great Plains toad find agreeable habitat in the Great Sand Hills.

Species lists for the Great Sand Hills, including the ones in this book, don't usually list insects but there is another world of wildlife to be found at that smaller scale. Ghost tiger beetles live here, preferring the same active dune habitat as Ord's kangaroo rat. It does not stay when dunes stabilize nor does it like smaller sandy areas such as blowouts and road cuts.

In 2003, researchers spent two three-day weekends in the Great Sand Hills collecting Orthoptera (grasshoppers and allied species) day and night. Even the researchers were surprised at the richness of their take, which included specimens of 58 species. Two species of band-winged grasshoppers (*Trimerotropis campestris* and *Trimerotropis agrestis*) are common in the Great Sand Hills but tough to find in most other settings.

The natural plant and animals communities of the Great Sand Hills are many and varied. Taken as a whole, they represent an amazingly diverse assemblage that has escaped the sweeping homogenization that was the fate of surrounding agricultural lands. But even here, for the last hundred years or so, there has been a new, active force on the Sand Hills ecosystem. Ranchers and their cattle have become entwined with the state and the fate of the Great Sand Hills.

Ranching and the Great Sand Hills

"Ranching is the traditional and the predominant land use activity within the Great Sand Hills area. It offers family members the opportunity to stay on the land and foster longstanding community relationships. With this long history, of ranching, grazing as a land use has been determined to be ecologically manageable and sustainable."

At least three generations gather at the Ian and Eleanor Bowie ranch near Piapot for the annual spring branding, eager to be part of a tradition dating back to 1912. Amid the noise, smoke and confusion, cowboys and their horses go calmly about the business of branding, tagging, and vaccinating 400 calves.

Ranching—responsible use of suitable land—in the Great Sand Hills has proven itself to be a long-term, ecologically sustainable use of the area's resources.

74

These statements from *The Great Sand Hills Land Use Strategy Review, Final Report and Recommendations* (June, 2004) pretty much say it all. As already discussed, ranchers are driven by economic reality to be good stewards of the land. The use of suitable land in the Great Sand Hills for grazing makes ecological sense if you consider that cattle in many ways fill the niche left vacant when bison were exterminated.

It may not be the first example that comes to mind but cattle dung replaced buffalo pies. Why would that be important? Burrowing owls lined their nest with bison dung. It helped to control the microclimate inside the burrow. They also collected the dung and spread it around near their burrow, then dined on the dung beetles it attracted. Today, cattle dung serves the same purposes admirably.

Burrowing owls, and some other species, prefer grazed areas where they can keep an eye out for predators. Again, cattle took over this job from the bison. Burrowing owls and cattle ranching fit together so well that Canada's Species at Risk Program states bluntly "Burrowing Owls depend on grazing." Loss of habitat on their breeding grounds is believed to be a large part of the reason burrowing owl populations have declined. Saskatchewan has the largest remaining population of burrowing owls in Canada, and owls born here spend their winters along the coastal lowlands of the Gulf of Mexico and in southern Texas.

During a single breeding season in Saskatchewan, a family of burrowing owls can consume 1,800 small rodents and crunch more than 7,000 insects, of which most are grasshoppers.

In the Great Sand Hills area, according to figures from Operation Burrowing Owl, 27 stewards on 64 sites are helping to conserve a total of 6,098 acres of breeding habitat. The ranchers benefit as well.

Cattle do not exactly replicate bison. Unlike bison, cattle don't make wallows. Cattle eat a slightly different mixture of plants than bison which, no doubt, has subtly altered the vegetation over time. Cattle spend more time seeking shelter from temperature extremes because they are less well adapted to the environment than the bison. For the same reason, they require more water in times of drought and tend to spend time in and around sloughs and creeks, which can have a significant negative impact on the water and the surrounding land.

The Great Sand Hills provide critical breeding habitat for the endangered burrowing owl. Twenty-seven area ranchers participate in the Operation Burrowing Owl stewardship program.

An awareness of these facts helps ranchers adjust routines to create or maintain suitable wildlife habitat. Rancher John Aitken has set up taps from a recent water development so that he can separate his grazing areas into tame and native forages, allowing him to shift his cattle to give the native prairie a rest until late summer. This not only gives the native grasses optimum growing conditions but provides critical nesting habitat for the Sprague's Pipit, a species listed as "threatened" by the Committee on the Status of Endangered Wildlife in Canada. Aitken ranches near Eyebrow, SK, outside the Great Sand Hills area, but the concept is certainly applicable here as well.

Ranching also conserves biodiversity. A study published in 2003 demonstrated that ranches had more diverse plant communities than all other types of land use surveyed, including nature reserves. Ranches also had the smallest percentage of non-native species. The researchers concluded "ranches are important for protecting biodiversity."

Ranching—responsible use of suitable land—in the Great Sand Hills has proven itself to be a long-term, ecologically sustainable use of the area's resources. This practical observation is supported by a growing amount of research. Ranchers are part of the Sand Hills—past, present, and, hopefully, future.

Where Do We Go from Here

Human interaction with the Great Sand Hills has grown in scale, particularly in the last 30 years since natural gas deposits began being developed, bringing new roads and more traffic. A photograph published on the SaskTel phone book introduced the whole province to the dunes, spurring an interest in tourism that continues to grow. Hunters come to the Sand Hills for deer and grouse.

Alongside a growing awareness and appreciation of how unique the Great Sand Hills are has come the offer of money for developing the natural gas resources beneath them. The arguments one way and another have been heated, emotional, and many-faceted.

The Great Sand Hills have always been different from the surrounding landscape and the ecological disparity between the two areas has grown larger over time. Today, the Sand Hills are effectively a 190,000 hectare island containing a irreplaceable combination and juxtaposition of ecosystems—an island with the waves of development slowly eating away at its shores.

What should be the future of the Great Sand Hills?

NO ENTRY

DON'T STRADDLE TRAIL

The Future

The current debate about development in the Great Sand Hills is not new. The first exploration and development of natural gas resources in the area dates back to the late 1970s. The natural gas found in the Great Sand Hills is particularly attractive to oil and gas companies because it is "sweet" gas, meaning it contains very little sulfur and requires less refining before being consumer-ready.

In 1978, Lawrence Townley-Smith prepared a preliminary report and study design for Saskatchewan Environment which led to the 1980 survey and report by H. T. Epp and Townley-Smith. This report, *The Great Sand Hills of Saskatchewan*, examined the ecology, archaeology, and current resource management of the area and made recommendations about future land use management. Epp and Townley-Smith provided a comprehensive overview but also indicated that knowledge of the area's ecological and archaeological resources was far from complete. After discussing the various types of land use in the Great Sand Hills, as well as conflicts between them based on differing priorities, they concluded their report with the opinion that:

> "*The Great Sand Hills of Saskatchewan are an example of a relatively undisturbed ecosystem which, if properly managed, can continue to provide economic benefits to the residents of this province while maintaining an important ecological and genetic reservoir of living systems and individuals well tuned to the harsh prairie environment through generations of adaptive process. Man has the power to destroy or preserve. The choice is ours!*"

While working on this book, I was fortunate enough to speak at some length with Lawrence Townley-Smith, now with Agriculture and Agri-Food Canada. I wondered if he still felt the same way about the Great Sand Hills twenty years down the road. He told me that when he was working on the report, he was impressed with the plant life,

The landscape is rugged but the land is fragile. The unique ecosystem found here contains delicate balances that have evolved together. Disrupt any part and you disrupt all.

(Left) An aerial view of the road leading to the parking lot for main visitor access to the Sand Hills. Ecotourism in the Great Sand Hills is a mixed blessing, bringing needed cash to surrounding communities but also taxing an already inadequate infrastructure.
(Right) The scars of an old road linger near Hazlet.

the wildlife, and the way people made a living on the land without really intruding on the environment. The area "sticks out like a sore thumb" on the prairies he said, emphasizing its uniqueness. Gas development was just getting underway in the Great Sand Hills when Townley-Smith last spent any length of time in the area; he hasn't been back recently except for a brief visit to the open dunes south of Sceptre. The image he holds of the area is still of the summer he spent there, camping in a tent and making new discoveries about the Sand Hills ecosystem every day. Watching his face as he talked, I could see that "his" Great Sand Hills are still a special place.

In 1990-1991, continuing conflict about what was best for the Great Sand Hills led the province to undertake a land use planning effort for the area. The province adopted the resulting set of recommendations, published in 1991 as *Great Sand Hills Land Use Strategy*, as management policy.

The *Strategy* proposed that the Great Sand Hills be classified into four different zones for the purposes of managing land use and development. The zones were Prime Protection Area, Special Use Area, Multiple Land Use Area, and Facility Area. The *Strategy* proposed that most of the area be considered multiple use which would allow a variety of uses, including gas development and ranching, subject to applicable regulatory procedures. It also proposed that about 4.6% of the area—three separate areas containing open, active dunes—be placed under some form of protection.

The Saskatchewan government did not follow the conservation recommendations of the report completely. Instead, they placed some of the Prime Protection Area and Special Use Area land, totaling 36.5 sections or 94.5 square kilometers, in Crown mineral reserve, meaning no mineral development was allowed. This land was in three widely separated blocks rather than one contiguous area and constituted 5% of the Great Sand Hills.

Debate over land use continued and ranchers in the area felt a need for more control over what was happening. In 1994, four rural municipalities (RMs) with the most land in the Great Sand Hills area—Piapot, Pittville, Fox Valley, and Clinworth—formed the Great Sand Hills Planning District Commission (GSHPDC). Working with the provincial government, industry, environmental groups and local people, the GSHPDC formulated a more specific land use plan. In 1998, a Joint Development Plan and joint zoning bylaws were adopted by the four RMs and approved by the province. The zoning system designated two environmentally sensitive zones plus a zone called agriculture reserve, in which most land uses would be allowed.

A horned lark appears to have its own opinion about the future of the Sand Hills.

In lands designated ES1 (Environmentally Sensitive 1), no oil and gas development nor other potentially detrimental uses were allowed. Nearly 118,000 hectares (455 sections) were zoned ES1. Surrounding ES1 lands were those classified as ES2 (Environmentally Sensitive 2). In these 306 sections (nearly 80,000 hectares), oil and gas development following special environmental specifications was allowed.

The Joint Development Plan was important because it was a local attempt to come up with a workable solution to the development problem by involving all the stakeholders in creating the plan. This local coalition came apart in 2000 when the RM of Piapot requested rezoning most of its ES1 lands to ES2 so that gas well development could proceed. The land in question was about 75 sections, which made up approximately one-quarter of the ES1 protected land in the Great Sand Hills. The RM also wished to rezone approximately 100 section of ES2 lands to Agricultural Reserve, which would allow most uses. These requests by the RM of Piapot prompted interest in rezoning from the other RMs. When news of these goings-on spread, the wind hit the sand.

Public pressure on the provincial government to protect the Great Sand Hills escalated as Piapot made a total of four unsuccessful attempts to gain approval to rezone from the GSHPDC. Piapot finally gave up and simply withdrew from the commission so that it could do what it wished.

In 2002, under continuing pressure, the province announced that it would initiate a review of the 1991 *Strategy*. A committee began holding closed-door meetings on the subject soon after but environmental groups and residents of the Great Sand Hills pushed to make the process open and accessible to the people concerned. The first public meetings were held in May and June, 2003, allowing people to present their ideas and opinions on the future of the Great Sand Hills. A report, *The Great Sand Hills Land Use Strategy Review*, summarizing the review committee's findings and recommendations was released in June 2004. The committee determined if various portions of the 1991 *Strategy* had been implemented and to what degree those implementations were complete. The committee then made recommendations for future land use management in the Great Sand Hills.

One of the most interesting things to come out of the review process dealt not directly with the Great Sand Hills but with the quality of interaction between the various groups involved, particularly the interactions between people and the government. People wanted more clarity from the government—better definition of terms and

These dunes lie near Yakowan in one of the few protected zones.

objectives; specification of provincial and municipal responsibilities; more opportunities for those involved to voice their questions and concerns and to receive answers. Letters submitted to the committee and discussion at the public meetings also made it clear that there was an underlying problem with trust in the review process and with belief in the government's willingness to listen to what people were telling them.

In general, the review committee's recommendations appear to accept that development will occur and therefore deal with how to control where and when. The first sentence of the Summary reads: "The Review Committee acknowledges that this is an opportunity for provincial and local governments to continue to work cooperatively to develop standards that not only protect the unique landscapes of the Great Sand Hills, but also to allow for the development of the gas reserves underlying the area and the grass resources on the surface."

One section of the recommendations lists the resources needed for monitoring and encouraging development. Another discusses the importance of streamlining the permitting process so that projects meeting the environmental requirements are not unduly delayed. The report does acknowledge that the committee was hampered by a lack of information about overall ecological impact of various land uses, and suggests that more data about the area be collected, including a survey of rare and endangered species. The committee also recommended that more land in the Great Sand Hills — roughly three times the amount already set aside—be protected.

> There was an underlying problem with trust in the review process and with belief in the government's willingness to listen to what people were telling them.

The Saskatchewan government announced that it would accept the recommendations. In March 2005, the province established the Great Sand Hills Representative Area Ecological Reserve, increasing the protected areas to 366 square kilometers—still less than 20% of the Great Sand Hills. The land was in four separate areas and the larger areas that had been protected as ES1 land under the GSHPDC plan were no longer protected. At the same time, the government promised to conduct an environmental review of the Great Sand Hills to gather more information upon which to base future decisions, and has since granted more than $2.5 million to fund the review process.

That review is the nearly completed Great Sand Hills Regional Environmental Study (GSHRES.) Besides conducting a survey of birds and plants in the area and gathering other environmental data, GSHRES has also been collecting information about the social and economic factors associated with the Great Sand Hills. From that information, the scientists will come up with risk assessments for various human activities in the area. In other words, how do those activities influence the social, economic, and environmental structures with which they interact? Using the risk factors they calculate, they will play through several scenarios for the future of the GSH, using different combinations of development and ecological preservation strategies. As a completely hypothetical example, since we are not privy to what scenarios they may be running, they might ask what happens to the local economy if we allow well development in 60% of the Sand Hills? Finally, according to the GSHRES *Terms of Reference*, the Scientific Advisory Committee will "provide analysis required to develop a strategy that maintains the ecological integrity of the Great Sand Hills based on principles of sustainable development." This means, as Committee Chair David Gauthier explained at a survey session I attended, that the committee will present to the Environment Minister the information they have gathered, the scenarios they have developed, and their recommendations for the scenario(s) they feel best meet the criteria of ecologically sustainable development. Gauthier apologized for being unable to say definitely how much of this information will be released to the public and when that might happen.

So, this is where we sit at the moment. The Saskatchewan government placed a moratorium on "all new mineral sales and new gas development in environmentally sensitive areas where mineral rights are undisposed" until the GSHRES is completed. Existing mineral rights would be honored and grazing could also continue. The moratorium did not stop plans for new well developments from entering the regulatory system, however, so that they would be ready for approval at the earliest possible moment. And the currently operating wells and new wells on previously leased sites are a continuing source of friction in the area.

I decided to talk with two people on opposing sides of the development debate to get some insight into what effect all of this was having on the lives of people who live in the Great Sand Hills area. I got in touch with John Wagner, Reeve of the RM of Piapot and driving force behind the decision for the RM to leave the GSHPDC, and with Eleanor Bowie, a rancher north of Piapot who is a member of the GSHPDC and was on the Great Sand Hills Land Use Strategy Review Committee.

A gas well on the Bowie ranch near Piapot.

Returning my call late one evening in the middle of harvest, John Wagner was happy to tell me his view of the situation. On the subject of Piapot leaving the GSHPDC, Wagner told me that the ES1 land had been zoned incorrectly in the first place and that, although there are places in the Sand Hills where wells shouldn't be drilled, this land could handle the carefully monitored gas drilling and production activity. He emphasized the strict supervision under which the companies are required to operate. When I enquired about economic benefits for the RM, Wagner pointed out that, although the majority of revenue from gas development goes to the province, money from the gas companies accounted for 50% of Piapot's property tax revenue. In addition, he said, developing this resource is bringing jobs to the area, including spin-offs to businesses like motels and welding shops, that will help to keep young people in the area. Wagner also added that several ranchers work part-time in various capacities for gas companies, giving them additional income that helps them keep ranching. He did feel that there should be slightly better compensation for leaseholders who have wells drilled on their land. (At present, they are given $100 for their trouble and are required to allow "reasonable" access to well sites.) In short, Wagner felt that development should occur in all but the most sensitive areas, could be done without causing lasting ecological damage, and believed that the revenue and economic spin-offs from the gas industry provided money essential for keeping the area alive and growing. Just before we ended our conversation, I asked Wagner if he wished to give me a quote about the issue for the book. Wagner replied, "In the Sand Hills, it's quite evident that ranching and the gas industry can work together."

Reclamation begins following pipeline placement. Gas companies may use several measures to reduce soil erosion during and after well and pipeline development. Due to the fragile nature of the terrain, their efforts meet with varying degrees of success.

Eleanor Bowie would beg to differ. Bowie and her husband, Ian, along with their son, Jon, run a ranch northwest of Piapot. The ranch has been in the Bowie family since 1912 and Eleanor has lived there for 35 years. Outspoken and articulate, Bowie has made presentation after presentation on the problems she sees with further development in the Sand Hills. When I spoke with her, Bowie told me that her biggest concern is the cumulative long-term impact of all the individual developments. She referred to it as "death by a thousand cuts." "Ranchers in the Great Sand Hills," she explained, "have four building blocks with which to work: the soil and climate, the water, the vegetative community, and the faunal community. Disrupt any of those and it disrupts them all."

The Bowies have wells on the grazing land they lease and are not happy with the gas companies' way of doing business. Referring to one company, Anadarko, Bowie snapped, "Their promises are as empty and as useful as the cavity in my back tooth!" She talked about the mess at well sites and the gravel dumped on roads to stabilize them. Along with the gravel, she said, come invasive plants.

Changing topics, I asked Bowie how she felt about the Great Sand Hills after interacting with it on a daily basis for so many years. There was a pause and then she told me that she has favorite spots in the hills. Being in those places, she continued, "is the closest I've come to touching the face of God." She didn't try to explain any further and I didn't ask her to. She did tell me a well had been drilled in one of those special places and that it was horrible to her now, like a "scar on the face of Mother Earth." Her voice choked and I could barely hear her as she said, "I feel like I should hold a funeral." For Bowie, more gas wells are not an acceptable option.

For yet another angle on the situation, I talked with Brian Mathieson at Industry and Resources Canada. Mathieson was the Co-Chair of the Great Sand Hills Land Use Strategy Review Committee and so was very familiar with the issues. After answering some specific questions I had about distribution of revenues and environmental regulations, he spoke about the Great Sand Hills. In his view, the natural gas resource should be and will be developed. But, he emphasized, that development should take place sensibly. He spoke about a project south of Maple Creek in which development decisions were made on a site-specific basis with the ranchers' cooperation. Mathieson suggested that this type of management would make more sense in the Great Sand Hills than the kind of large-area zoning applied by the GSHPDC.

Just when I began the work of actually putting this book on paper, I received a phone call from a man who identified himself as Edwin Small Legs of the Piikani Blackfoot First Nation. I knew of him from a mutual friend and also of his interest in the Great Sand Hills. Small Legs believes that the sacred nature of the Great Sand Hills to his people must be considered in any plan for their future. It is part of the traditional Blackfoot culture that must be preserved, he stated, especially considering how much was taken away. Small Legs is seeking the support of the Blackfeet of Montana in his effort to make his voice heard in the Great Sand Hills debate. For him it is a very personal issue. "I will be with my ancestors there when I die," he told me. "That belief is part of me spiritually, part of me culturally, and the Great Sand Hills are sacred land to me."

Many voices, many opinions, many different, often conflicting, visions of the future. What will happen in the Great Sand Hills? The area and its resources belong to all the people of Saskatchewan and there are some important things we should consider when we are planning for the future.

Revenue from Natural Gas

According to a 2005 Burlington Resources environmental impact statement for their proposed development near Freehold Lake in the Great Sand Hills, as of 2001, the 1,213 producing natural gas wells in the Great Sand Hills Planning District were generating annual revenue to the province of more than $5.5 million. The provincial government has been eager to encourage gas and oil development in Saskatchewan— so eager that they have been accused by some of virtually giving away a non-renewable resource that took millions of years to form. Prior to 1981 the natural gas industry in Saskatchewan paid royalties of less than four percent of sales. That rose to 13 percent in 1990 and topped out at 15 percent towards the ends of the Romanow government. In 2002, Lorne Calvert's government announced large tax breaks and royalty cuts for the oil, gas, and mining industries. This, as John Warnock points out in *Saskatchewan:*

This natural gas compressor station is located northwest of Piapot.

The Roots of Discontent and Protest, at a time when oil and gas prices were on a steady climb and shortages were appearing. At the end of 2003, just before provincial elections, Eric Cline—then and now NDP Minister of Industry and Resources—announced that new oil and gas wells pay a maximum royalty of 2.5 percent on Crown land and 0.0 percent on private land. Interestingly enough, in 1991 long-time NDP party official Mark Stobbe had been extremely critical of a similar although far less dramatic royalty reduction policy by Grant Devine's government. He was writing specifically about oil but his arguments apply equally well to natural gas:

> *"Oil is a finite, non-renewable resource. If left in the ground, it increases in value. While giving oil away may not result in any immediate drop in revenue, in the medium and long-term the province has given away a nonrenewable resource without receiving any compensation in return. Further, by making the production*

from new wells royalty-free, the government encourages oil companies to artificially shift production from old wells to new ones. This creates a few drilling jobs, but makes no long-term economic sense. The royalty structure encourages waste and inefficiency by giving an incentive to producers to restrict output from existing wells while drilling new wells in the same field."

The current Saskatchewan government would do well to consider their own arguments. As Warnock states, "It seems fairly clear that the people of Saskatchewan are receiving a bare minimum for the exploitation of non-renewable natural resources by the large transnational corporations." The natural gas under the Great Sand Hills certainly won't *decrease* in value as it sits there. Once drilled, how long will wells in the area produce gas and, therefore, revenue? Burlington Resources estimates a well life of approximately 25 years for the 1,213 wells in operation in the Great Sand Hills as of 2001.

Water in a Thirsty Land

In the Great Sand Hills, water is a critical resource for the ranching industry. Without water for their cattle, ranchers are out of business. Water sources developed for cattle also provide a welcome drink for wildlife. Clearly, preserving water quality and quantity should be a prime consideration during any discussion of land use in the Sand Hills.

The shallow near surface aquifers found in the Great Sand Hills, particularly those shallow enough to be accessed with a sand point well, are highly vulnerable to contamination. According to gas company project proposals as well as statements from municipal and provincial officials, gas companies are using best management practices and taking special care to ensure there are no leaks or spills during well development or production. However, should a spill or leak of drilling fluids or other chemical contaminant occur, the highly permeable nature of the sand and gravel aquifers would allow it to spread easily.

It takes water to drill a well, for mixing drilling mud if nothing else. That water is usually taken from local sources. The amount required for developing one well may not seem like much but a large number of drilling projects may place a significant additional demand on existing water supplies. In areas such as the Sand Hills where water is not abundant, this can be a cause for concern. The projected cumulative water demand of any kind of development must be taken into account.

Water sources like this stock tank benefit not only a rancher's cattle but also wildlife.

A spring storm leaves behind water in the fields east of Fox Valley (right) and a windmill stands sentinel-like over a well-used waterhole (left). Surface water in the Great Sand Hills is often a "here today, gone tomorrow" resource becasue of the permeable nature of the soil.

Water in the Great Sand Hills is both valuable and vulnerable. Currently, it sustains both the ranching industry and the unique ecosystem of the area in a relationship that has evolved over the years. Development posing a potential threat to this critical resource should be considered with extreme caution if at all.

The Danger of Going to Pieces

"The Commission has suggested on numerous occasions that an effective trail management plan that reduces the number of trails, rutting, trail reclamation, minimizing trail blowouts, and other concerns be addressed. It is important to recognize that such a plan would apply to all users, including ranchers, hunters and RM road policies. Some trails, which are not intended for public use, are desirable to trespassing and recreational vehicles that do further damage to the trails above and beyond ranching and gas industry use. There are concerns that ecotourism may actually be more harmful by making the area overly accessible to more recreational activities that may cause as much disturbance as other defined developments. All of these concerns should be addressed in further detail." — Great Sand Hills Land Use Strategy Review Report and Recommendations (2004)

Habitat fragmentation is deadly, sometimes acutely so as this meadowlark shows. The tremendous value of the Great Sand Hills lies in its relatively unbroken area of habitat. Each additional road or path exposes new areas to erosion and invasive species as well as to more direct threats like vehicle traffic.

Perhaps the most often-proclaimed asset of the Great Sand Hills is that it is a large, *contiguous* area of relatively undisturbed land. Habitat fragmentation—splitting up habitat with roads, utility corridors, trails—is the biggest threat to most species today, not just in the Sand Hills but globally. Fragmenting habitat makes it less attractive to many species. Breaks in habitat make it difficult for young animals (especially small terrestrial species) to find territories and mates. Fragmentation also increases the relative percentage of edge habitat, which increases vulnerability to invasive plant species and makes the area more attractive to predators such as coyotes, which like to hunt along habitat boundaries.

The Great Sand Hills are especially vulnerable because they exist in a fragile state of balance. It is the combination of ecosystems and the interaction of their inhabitants, as well as the relatively intact nature of those ecosystems that makes the Great Sand Hills so unique and important. Only a thin vegetative cover stands between stabilized hills and blowing sand. Each break in the cover is another chance for the wind to eat away at the land. There is a danger of looking at new developments in the Sand Hills on individual basis and seeing them as relatively benign—a new trail here, some vegetation removed there. For the Sand Hills this could truly be, as Eleanor Bowie

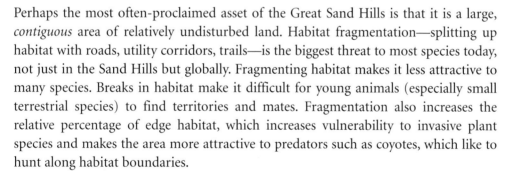

Ruts made by truck traffic through a pasture show saline deposits left behind when water evaporates from the exposed ground. Breaching the surface vegetation in the Great Sand Hills can cause problems other than simple erosion.

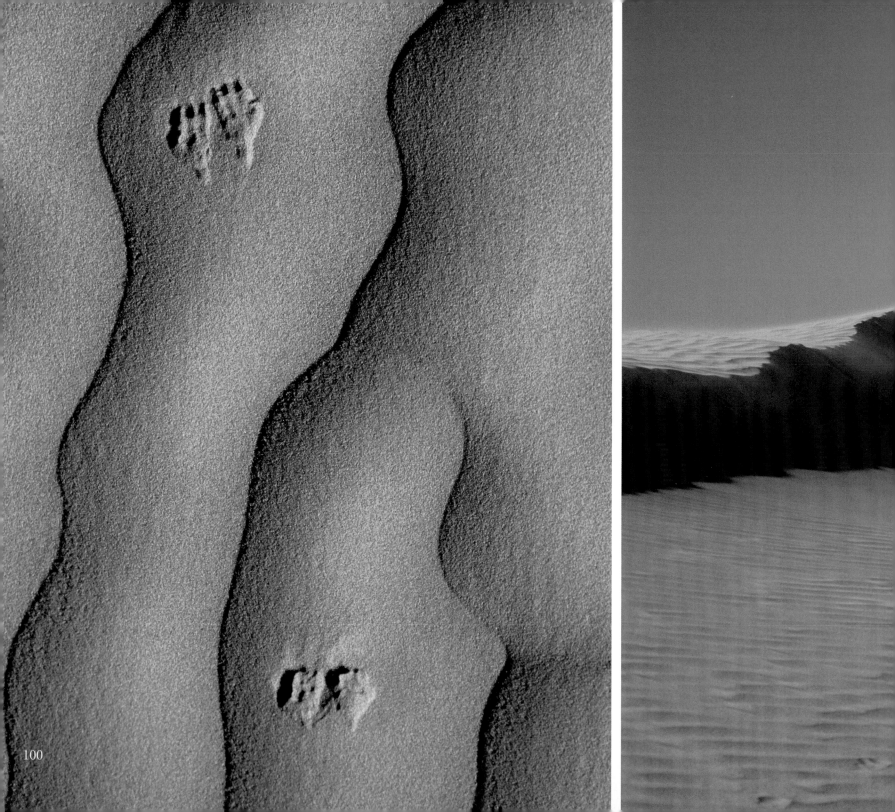

The sand shifts incessantly with the touch of the wind and tracks disappear leaving no trace. But life in the Great Sand Hills ticks on at its own rhythm, from day to day and season to season, as it has for thousands of years.

101

described it, "death by a thousand cuts." It is vital to consider the cumulative effects of all human activities—ranching, hunting, ecotourism, well development, road maintenance, pipeline maintenance, utility right-of-ways, even cattle trails. At the GSHRES study session I attended, we were shown a map of all trails and roads in the Great Sand Hills. It looked like the back of my sun-dried hand with closely-spaced lines cutting every which way across the surface. Each of those was a break in the vegetative cover that holds the land together. Each of those was a cut in the skin of the Great Sand Hills—how close are we to one thousand already?

Shifting Sands

In a volume of papers entitled *Managing Prairie Landscapes* (2005), one of the recurring themes was concern about the effect climate change will have on the prairies. Already, average annual temperatures across the Great Plains have risen by between 1.6°C and 2.8°C since 1961. Relatively conservative climate change models are predicting that, by the 2050s, average annual temperatures on the Canadian Prairies will increase 2.5° to 5.0°C and all seasons will be warmer. Remember the statement by Epp and Townley-Smith on the value of the Great Sand Hills as a reservoir of species that are adapted to cope with dry prairie environments.

The warming climate will almost certainly effect sand dune areas such as the Great Sand Hills by increasing the possibility of dune reactivation and the potential for soil erosion. Increasing their vulnerability further by exposing more surface area through increased development should not be done without due consideration of the consequences in a changing climate.

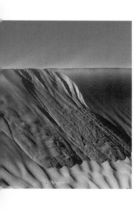

We can choose to protect the Great Sand Hills or let them slip away, bit by bit, on the winds of expediency.

A new report by the United Nations' Intergovernmental Panel on Climate Change (IPCC) is due to be released early in 2007. Andrew Weaver, a contributor to the report, is a leading Canadian climate researcher and holds the Canada research chair at the University of Victoria's school of earth and ocean sciences. In a September, 2006

statement to the press, Weaver said that the report will demonstrate such a convincing link between global warming and fossil fuels that "the world will have to end its addiction to oil." He added that the IPCC will stress the urgent need for national governments to cut back emissions from burning coal, oil, and natural gas. Perhaps this report will move the Saskatchewan government to invest in clean, renewable sources of energy rather than in tax breaks and royalty cuts for industries contributing to the climate change problem.

Choosing Our Path

Walking alone through the Great Sand Hills, the choice about further development seems obvious. This place should be kept as it is. I imagine it's a different story for those trying to balance the books at the rural municipalities, attempting to figure out how to provide vital services despite a declining and aging population. I have struggled to reach a final decision on what I believe is the right thing, based on facts as well as "gut feelings."

The ranchers in the Great Sand Hills have a relationship with the land that allows them to make a living with very minimal disruption to the environment. The water sources they provide for their cattle actually make the area more attractive for wildlife. The same cannot be said for the gas industry despite their best intentions, and even given their employment of special sensitive land drilling and development practices. There is a danger that well development could harm the two resources critical to the ranching industry, the water and the vegetation. There should be no further gas exploration and development in the Great Sand Hills. Ranching, along with controlled ecotourism and hunting, do and will contribute revenue to both provincial and municipal coffers on a long-term, sustainable basis.

Everyone must make up their own minds on this issue. Those that live in the Great Sand Hills and will be dealing on a day-to-day basis with the results of whatever decision is made should have the loudest voice, but all of us who live in Saskatchewan should be heard. The provincial government is there to manage our resources in our best interests, not theirs—unless we give them no direction. They have made a strong step in the right direction by acquiring as much information as possible on which to base future plans for the Great Sand Hills. It would be helpful if they would make that information available to the public that paid for it and who may be interested in the data for a variety of reasons, including coming to their own decision about development in the Great Sand Hills.

The NDP government knows the value of the Great Sand Hills. Once again, we can turn to the words of long-time NDP party official Mark Stobbe, who wrote in 1991:

> One of the important environmental issues emerging in Saskatchewan is the Conservative government's decisions to sell mineral rights to gas and oil companies in the Great Sand Hills, located west of Swift Current.
>
> This unique ecosystem has been designated by the World Wildlife Fund as one of Canada's wilderness areas most in need of protection. Farmers in the area are concerned that clearing land for gas pipelines and well sites will cause erosion and destroy sensitive vegetation. Local residents are also concerned that road construction leading to the gas wells will harm wildlife and make the area more accessible to hunters.
>
> Despite these concerns, the Conservative government is ignoring a 1980 study by the Saskatchewan Department of the Environment which concluded that the Sand Hills' ecosystem of rolling hills, sand dunes, and unique vegetation "is intolerant of greater than natural physical disturbance." In addition, the government is also ignoring requests from the Saskatchewan Natural History Society [now Nature Saskatchewan] to designate the area as a parkland or an ecological reserve.

What has changed now besides the name of the party in power?

It takes only the most fleeting visit to realize that the Great Sand Hills are extraordinary. Visitors with a knowledge of biology or botany come away awestruck at all that this area encompasses. There is always something unexpected over the hill. The Great Sand Hills ecosystem is unbelievably rich, especially when compared with the surrounding lands. History runs deep here and the area holds valuable archaeological sites just beginning to be explored. We can preserve this treasure: not as a static, glassed-in museum exhibit but as an example of humans working and making a living as a contributing part of an intricate, interwoven, living, breathing ecosystem. Like the Great Sand Hills themselves, that is truly unique.

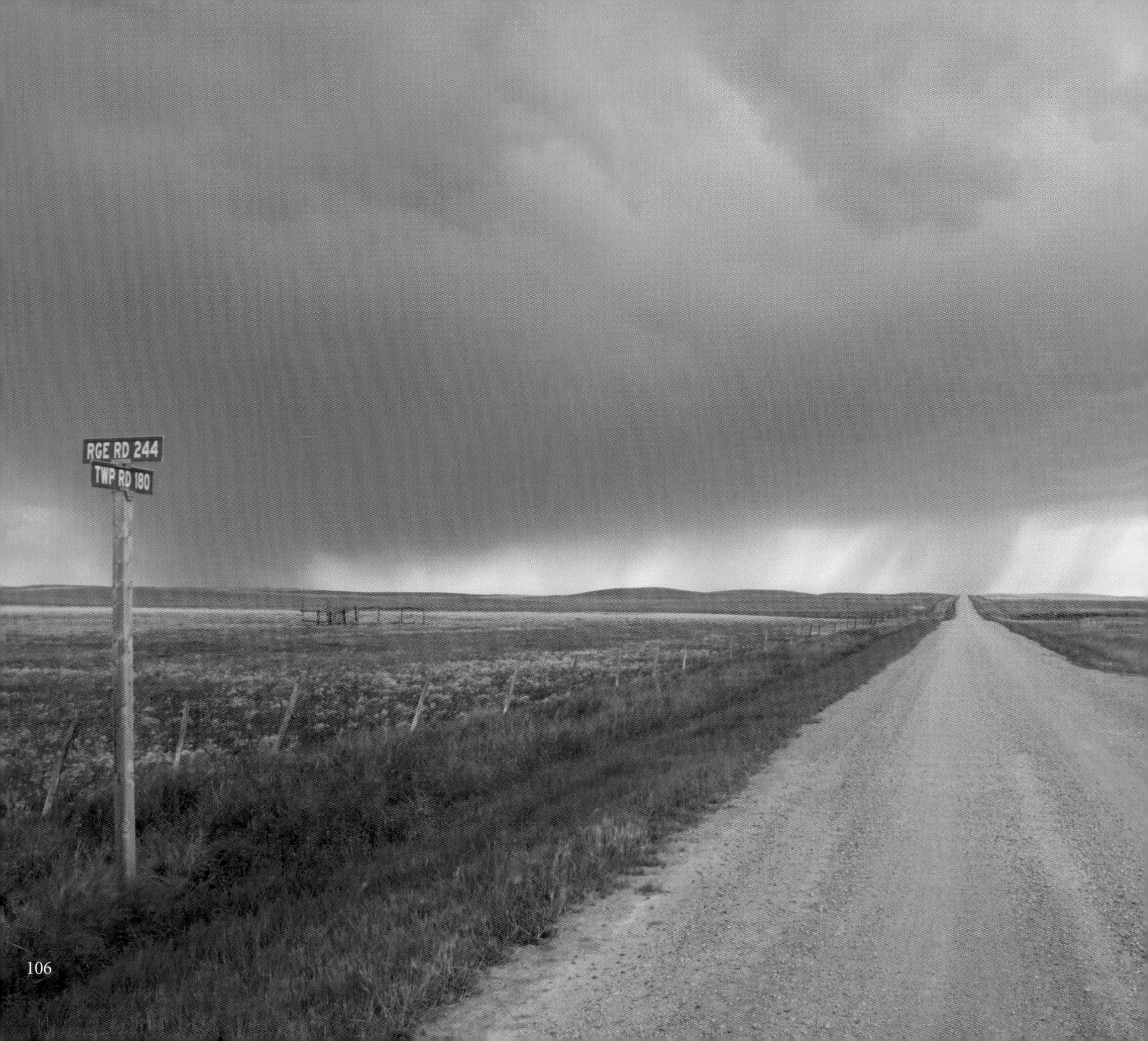
RGE RD 244
TWP RD 180

Plant Species Found in the Great Sand Hills

Sources: Epp and Townley-Smith (1980), Western Oilfield Environmental Services (1992), and Burlington Resources (2005).

SCIENTIFIC NAME	COMMON NAME
Acer negundo	Manitoba Maple, Box Elder
Achillea millefolium	Common Yarrow
Achillea millifolium var. occidentalis	Wooly Yarrow
Acroptilon repens (syn. Centaurea repens)	Russian Knapweed *Non-native*, Noxious
Agropyron cristatum (syn. Agropyron pectiniforme)	Crested Wheatgrass *Non-native*, Potentially Highly Invasive
Agropyron dasystachyum	Northern Wheatgrass
Agropyron repens (syn. Elytrigia repens)	Couch Grass, Quackgrass *Non-native*
Agropyron smithii (syn. Pascopyrum smithii)	Western Wheatgrass
Agropyron trachycaulum	Slender Wheatgrass
Agropyron trachycaulum var. unilaterale	Awned Wheatgrass
Agroseris glauca	False Dandelion
Agrostis scabra	Rough Hairgrass
Alisma gramineum	Narrow-leaved Water Plantain S3
Alisma plantago-aquatica	Broad-leaved Water Plantain
Allium textile	Prairie Onion
Ambrosia acanthicarpa (syn. Franseria acanthicarpa)	Bur Ragweed, Annual Bursage, Burweed S2
Amelanchier alnifolia	Saskatoon, Serviceberry, Juneberry, Shadbush
Andropogon hallii	Sand Bluestem
Andropogon scoparius	Little Bluestem Grass
Androsace septentrionalis	Pygmyflower, Rockjasmine
Anemone cylindrica	Long-fruited Anemone, Thimbleweed
Anemone multifida	Cut-leaved Anemone
Anemone patens	Crocus Anemone, Prairie Crocus, Pasqueflower
Antennaria dimorpha	Low Pussytoes S2
Antennaria microphylla	Pink Pussytoes, Rosy Pussytoes, Littleleaf pussytoes, Everlasting
Antennaria nitida	Littleleaf Pussytoes, White Pussytoes, Small-flowered Everlasting
Arabis holboellii	Holboell's Rockcress
Arctostaphylos uva-ursi	Bearberry, Kinnikinnick
Arenaria lateriflora	Blunt-leaved Sandwort
Artemisia absinthium	Wormwood, Madderwort, Mugwort, Sagebrush *Non-native*
Artemisia cana	Hoary Sagebrush, Silver Sagebrush
Artemisia frigida	Pasture Sage

Noxious	Listed under the Saskatchewan Noxious Weeds Act
S listing	Status as rated by Saskatchewan Conservation Data Centre
S1	Extremely Rare
S2	Rare
S3	Rare to Uncommon
S4	Common
Wildlife Act	Listed or pending listing under the Saskatchewan Wildlife Act
SARA	Listed or pending listing under the Species at Risk Act

Artemisia ludoviciana	Prairie Sage, White Sagebrush
Asclepias speciosa	Showy Milkweed
Aster laevis	Smooth Aster
Aster pansus	Many-flowered Aster, Small Clustered Aster
Astragalus agrestis	Purple Milk-vetch
Astragalus canadensis	Canadian Milk-vetch
Astragalus kentrophyta	Prickly Milk-vetch, Spiny Milk-vetch S1, Wildlife Act
Astragalus lotiflorus	Low Milk-vetch, Lotus Milk-vetch S3
Astragalus missouriensis	Missouri Milk-vetch
Astragalus pectinatus	Narrow-leaved Milk-vetch
Astragalus purshii	Pursh's Milk-vetch, Wooly Pod Milk-vetch S2
Astragalus striatus	Ascending Purple Milk-vetch
Atriplex nuttallii	Nuttall's Saltbush
Atriplex truncata	Wedge-scale Saltbush S1
Beckmannia syzigachne	Slough Grass
Betula occidentalis	River Birch
Botrychium campestre	Plains Grape-fern, Prairie Moonwort, Prairie Dunewort S1, Wildlife Act
Bouteloua gracilis	Blue Grama Grass
Bromus inermis	Smooth Brome Non-native, Potentially Highly Invasive
Bromus tectorum	Downy Brome, Cheatgrass Non-native, Noxious
Calamagrostis inexpansa	Northern Reed Grass
Calamagrostis montanensis	Plains Reed Grass
Calamagrostis neglecta	Narrow Reed Grass
Calamovilfa longifolia	Sand Reed Grass, Prairie Sandreed
Campanula rotundifolia	Harebell, Bluebell of Scotland
Caragana arborescens	Common Caragana, Siberian Peashrub Non-native
Carduus nutans	Nodding Thistle, Musk Thistle Non-native, Noxious
Carex douglasii	Douglas' Sedge
Carex filifolia	Thread-leaved Sedge
Carex oederi	Green Sedge
Carex peckii	Peck's Sedge
Carex pensylvanica	Pennsylvania Sedge, Yellow Sedge
Carex rossii	Ross' Sedge
Carex scirpoidea	Single Spike Sedge
Carex sprengelii	Sprengel's Sedge
Carex stenophylla	Low Sedge, Dryland Sedge
Cerastium arvense	Field Chickweed, Starry Cerastium
Cerastium nutans	Long-stalked Chickweed, Nodding Chickweed
Chenopodium album	Lambsquarters, Pigweed, Goosefoot Non-native
Chenopodium fremontii	Fremont's Goosefoot
Chenopodium hybridum	Maple-leaved Goosefoot
Chenopodium leptophyllum	Narrow-leaved Goosefoot
Chenopodium subglabrum	Smooth Goosefoot S2, SARA, Wildlife Act

Cleome serrulata
Spiderflower, Rocky Mountain Beeplant, Stinking Clover

Noxious — Listed under the Saskatchewan Noxious Weeds Act

S listing — Status as rated by Saskatchewan Conservation Data Centre

    S1 — Extremely Rare

    S2 — Rare

    S3 — Rare to Uncommon

    S4 — Common

Wildlife Act — Listed or pending listing under the Saskatchewan Wildlife Act

SARA — Listed or pending listing under the Species at Risk Act

Scientific name	Common name
Chrysopsis villosa	Hairy Golden Aster
Cirsium arvense	Canada Thistle *Non-native*, **Noxious**
Cirsium flodmanii	Flodman's Thistle, Prairie Thistle
Cirsium undulatum	Wavy-leaved Thistle
Clematis ligusticifolia	Western Virgin's Bower, Western White Clematis
Cleome serrulata	Spiderflower, Rocky Mountain Beeplant, Stinking Clover
Comandra pallida	Pale Bastard Toadflax
Comandra umbellata	Bastard Toadflax, False Toadflax
Convolvulus arvensis	Field Bindweed *Non-native*, **Noxious**
Coryphantha vivipara	Pincushion Cactus
Corispermum hyssopifolium	Bugseed
Corispermum orientale	Villose Bugseed, Wingless Bugseed S2
Cornus stolonifera (syn. Cornus sericea)	Red Osier Dogwood
Crepis runcinata	Smooth Hawksbeard, Fiddleleaf Hawksbeard
Cymopterus acaulis	Plains Cymopterus, Stemless Cymopterus
Cyperus schweinitzii	Schweinitz's Flatsedge, Great Plains Sand Sedge S2
Deschampsia caespitosa	Tufted Hairgrass
Descurainia pinnata	Short-fruited Tansymustard, Western Tansymustard
Descurainia richardsonii (syn. Descurainia incana)	Gray Tansymustard, Richardson's Tansymustard
Descurainia sophia	Flixweed, Common Tansymustard *Non-native*
Distichlis stricta	Alkali Grass, Saltgrass
Dodecatheon pauciflorum	Saline Shooting Star
Downingia laeta	Great Basin Calicoflower, Bright Downingia
Draba nemorosa	Yellow Whitlow-grass, Woodland Whitlow-grass
Elaeagnus commutata	Silverberry, Wolf Willow
Elymus canadensis	Canada Wild Rye
Elymus elymoides	Bottlebrush, Squirreltail S2
Epilobium glandulosum	Northern Willow Herb
Equisetum arvense	Common Horsetail
Equisetum hyemale	Common Scouring Rush
Equisetum laevigatum	Smooth Scouring Rush, Smooth Horsetail
Erigeron canadensis (syn. Conyza canadensis)	Canada Fleabane, Horseweed, Bitterweed
Erigeron pumilus	Hairy Daisy, Shaggy Fleabane
Erysimum asperum	Western Wallflower
Erysimum inconspicuum	Small-flowered Prairie Rocket, Shy Wallflower
Festuca ovina	Sheep Fescue, Blue Fescue
Gaillardia aristata	Blanket Flower, Great-flowered Gaillardia
Gaura coccinea	Scarlet Gaura, Scarlet Butterfly Weed
Gentiana affinis	Oblong-leaved Gentian, Rocky Mountain Gentian, Northern Gentian, Prairie Gentian
Geum triflorum	Three-flowered Avens, Prairie Smoke, Purple Avens, Old Man's Beard
Glaux maritima	Sea Milkwort

Glycyrrhiza lepidota	Wild Licorice
Grindelia squarrosa	Gum Weed, Curlycup Gumweed
Gutierrezia sarothrae	Broomweed, Broom Snakeweed
Habenaria nyperborea	Green-flowered Bog Orchid, Northern Green Orchid
Hackelia americana	Nodding Stickseed, American Stickseed
Hackelia floribunda	Large-flowered Stickseed, Manyflower Stickseed
Helianthus maximilianii	Narrow-leaved Sunflower, Prairie Sunflower, Maximillian Sunflower
Helianthus petiolaris	Prairie Sunflower, Plains Sunflower
Heliotropium curassavicum	Spatulate-leaved heliotrope, Salt Heliotrope, Seaside Heliotrope
Hesperostipa comata (syn. Stipa comata)	Needle-and-Thread Grass, Spear Grass
Heuchera richardsonii	Richardson's Alumroot, Prairie Alumroot
Hordeum jubatum	Wild Barley, Foxtail Barley
Iva xanthifolia	Giant Sumpweed, False Ragweed *Non-native*
Juncus balticus	Baltic Rush
Juncus longistylis	Long-styled Rush
Juniperus communis	Low Juniper, Common Juniper
Juniperus horizontalis	Creeping Juniper
Koeleria cristata	Junegrass
Lactuca pulchella	Blue Lettuce
Lappula occidentalis	Western Bluebur, Flatspine Stickseed, Western Sticktight
Lappula squarrosa	Bluebur, European Stickseed *Non-native*, Noxious
Lobelia kalmii	Kalm's Lobelia, Brook Lobelia, Bog Lobelia
Lepidium densiflorum	Common Pepper Grass, Common Pepperweed
Lesquerella arenosa	Sand Bladderpod, Great Plains Bladderpod
Liatris ligulistylis	Meadow Blazing Star, Rocky Mountain Blazing Star
Liatris punctata	Dotted Blazing Star, Narrow-leaved Blazing Star, Dotted Gayfeather
Lilium philadelphicum	Wood Lily, Western Red Lily
Linum lewisii	Lewis' Wild Flax, Blue Flax, Prairie Flax
Linum rigidum	Large-flowered Yellow Flax, Stiffstem Flax
Lithospermum incisum	Narrow-leaved Puccoon, Narrowleaf Stoneseed
Lupinus pusillus	Small Lupine, Rusty Lupine S3, Wildlife Act
Lygodesmia rostrata (syn. Shinneroseris rostrata)	Beaked Annual Skeleton-weed S1/S2, Wildlife Act
Lygodesmia juncea	Skeletonweed, Rush Skeletonplant
Mamillaria vivipara	Ball Cactus, Cushion Cactus
Medicago sativa	Alfalfa, Lucerne *Non-native*
Melilotus alba	White Sweet Clover *Non-native*
Mentha arvensis	Wild Mint
Mirabilis hirsuta	Hairy Umbrellawort, Hairy Four O'Clock S2
Mirabilis linearis	Linear-leaved umbrellawort, Narrowleaf Four O'Clock S2
Muhlenbergia asperifolia	Scratchgrass
Muhlenbergia richardsonis	Mat Muhly
Navarretia leucocephala var. minima	Pin-cushion Plant, Least Navarretia S2/S3
Oenothera nuttallii	White Evening-primrose, Nuttall's Evening-primrose

Orobanche fasciculata
Clustered Broomrape

Noxious	Listed under the Saskatchewan Noxious Weeds Act
S listing	Status as rated by Saskatchewan Conservation Data Centre
S1	Extremely Rare
S2	Rare
S3	Rare to Uncommon
S4	Common
Wildlife Act	Listed or pending listing under the Saskatchewan Wildlife Act
SARA	Listed or pending listing under the Species at Risk Act

Salix bebbiana	Beaked Willow, Bebb's Willow
Salix brachycarpa	Short-capsuled Willow, Barrenground Willow
Salix interior	Sandbar Willow, Long Leaf Willow
Salix lutea	Yellow Willow
Salsola kali (syn. Salsola australis)	Russian Thistle, Tumbleweed *Non-native*, Noxious
Scirpus nevadensis	Nevada Bulrush
Scirpus paludosus	Prairie Bulrush, Bayonet Grass, Salt Marsh Bulrush
Scirpus validus	Great Bulrush, Softstem Bulrush
Selaginella densa	Prairie Selaginella, Lesser Spikemoss, Small Clubmoss
Senecio canus	Silvery Groundsel, Woolly Groundsel
Senecio pauperculus	Balsam Groundsel
Senecio pseudaureus	Thin-leaved Ragwort, Western Golden Groundsel, S1
Senecio vulgaris	Common Groundsel
Shepherdia argentea	Silver Buffaloberry
Salicornia rubra	Red Samphire, Red Swampfire
Silene noctiflora	Night-flowering Catchfly
Sisyrinchium montanum	Common Blue-eyed Grass
Sium suave	Water Parsnip
Smilacina stellata	Star-flowered Solomon's Seal, False Solomon's Seal
Solidago missouriensis	Prairie Goldenrod, Missouri Goldenrod
Solidago mollis	Velvety Goldenrod
Sonchus arvensis	Perennial Sow Thistle *Non-native*
Sonchus asper	Prickly Sow Thistle, Spiny Sow Thistle
Spartina gracilis	Alkali Cordgrass
Spergularia marina	Salt-marsh Sand Spurry
Sphaeralcea coccinea	Scarlet Globemallow
Sporobolus cryptandrus	Sand Dropseed
Stellaria longipes	Longstalk Starwort
Symphoricarpos occidentalis	Western Snowberry
Tanacetum vulgare	Common Tansy *Non-native*
Taraxacum officinale	Common Dandelion *Non-native*, Noxious
Thermopsis rhombifolia	Golden Bean, Buffalo Bean
Thlaspi arvense	Stinkweed, Pennycress *Non-native*, Noxious
Townsendia sericea	Low Townsendia
Tragopogon dubius	Yellow Goat's–beard, Yellow Salsify *Non-native*
Triglochin maritime	Seaside Arrow Grass
Tripleurospermum perforatum	Scentless Chamomile *Non-native*
Typha latifolia	Common Cattail
Vicia americana (syn. Vicia sparsifolia)	American Vetch
Viola adunca	Blue violet, Western Dog Violet, Hookedspur Violet
Viola glabella	Yellow Violet, Pioneer Violet, Stream Violet
Vulpia octoflora	Six-weeks Fescue S1/S2
Yucca glauca	Soapweed Yucca *Non-native*

Sphaeralcea coccinea
Scarlet Globemallow

Animal Species Found in the Great Sand Hills

Sources: Saskatchewan Environment Online Saskatchewan Bird Atlas. Bird species names from American Ornithologists Union Check-list of North American Birds (2006). Also Epp and Townley-Smith (1980).

SCIENTIFIC NAME	COMMON NAME
MAMMALS	
Lasionycteris noctivagans	Silver-haired Bat
Sylvilagus nuttallii	Nuttall's Cottontail
Lepus townsendii	White-tailed Jack Rabbit
Spermophilus richardsonii	Richardson's Ground Squirrel (around area margins)
Spermophilus tridecemlineatus	Thirteen-lined Ground Squirrel
Thomomys talpoides	Northern Pocket Gopher
Perognathus fasciatus	Olive-backed Pocket Mouse S3
Dipodomys ordii	Ord's Kangaroo Rat S2, Wildlife Act, SARA
Peromyscus maniculatus	Deer Mouse
Clethrionomys gapperi	Gapper's Red-backed Vole, Southern Red-backed Vole
Ondatra zibethicus	Muskrat
Microtus pennsylvanicus	Meadow Vole
Erethizon dorsatum	American Porcupine
Canis latrans	Coyote
Mustela frenata	Long-tailed Weasel S3/S4
Taxidea taxus	American Badger S3/S4
Odocoileus hemionus	Mule Deer
Odocoileus virginianus	White-tailed Deer
Antilocapra americana	Pronghorn
AMPHIBIANS	
Ambystoma tigrinum	Tiger Salamander
Scaphiopus bombifrons	Plains Spadefoot Toad S3
Bufo hemiophrys	Canadian Toad
Bufo cognatus	Great Plains Toad S3, Wildlife Act, SARA
Rana pipiens	Northern Leopard Frog SARA
BIRDS	
Podilymbus podiceps	Pied-billed Grebe
Podiceps auritus	Horned Grebe
Podiceps nigricollis	Eared Grebe
Aechmophorus occidentalis	Western Grebe
Pelecanus erythrorhynchos	American White Pelican S3B
Phalacrocorax auritus	Double-crested Cormorant
Botaurus lentiginosus	American Bittern

S listing	Status as rated by Saskatchewan Conservation Data Centre
S1	Extremely Rare
S2	Rare
S3	Rare to Uncommon
S4	Common
Wildlife Act	Listed or pending listing under the Saskatchewan Wildlife Act
SARA	Listed or pending listing under the Species at Risk Act

Ixobrychus exilis	Least Bittern S1
Ardea herodias	Great Blue Heron
Egretta thula	Snowy Egret
Nycticorax nycticorax	Black-crowned Night Heron
Plegadis falcinellus	Glossy Ibis S1
Plegadis chihi	White-faced Ibis
Anser albifrons	Greater White-fronted Goose
Chen caerulescens	Snow Goose
Chen rossii	Ross' Goose
Branta canadensis	Canada Goose
Cygnus buccinator	Trumpeter Swan
Cygnus columbianus	Tundra Swan
Anas strepera	Gadwall
Anas americana	American Wigeon
Anas platyrhynchos	Mallard
Anas discors	Blue-winged Teal
Anas cyanoptera	Cinnamon Teal
Anas clypeata	Northern Shoveler
Anas acuta	Northern Pintail
Anas crecca	Green-winged Teal
Aythya valisineria	Canvasback
Aythya americana	Redhead
Aythya collaris	Ring-necked Duck
Aythya affinis	Lesser Scaup
Melanitta fusca	White-winged Scoter
Bucephala albeola	Bufflehead
Bucephala clangula	Common Goldeneye
Mergus serrator	Red-breasted Merganser
Oxyura jamaicensis	Ruddy Duck
Circus cyaneus	Northern Harrier (Marsh Hawk)
Accipiter striatus	Sharp-shinned Hawk
Accipter cooperii	Cooper's Hawk S4B, S2M, S2N
Buteo swainsoni	Swainson's Hawk
Buteo jamaicensis	Red-tailed Hawk
Buteo regalis	Ferruginous Hawk S4B, S4M, SARA
Buteo lagopus	Rough-legged Hawk
Aquila chrysaetos	Golden Eagle S3B, S4M, S3N
Falco sparverius	American Kestrel
Falco columbarius	Merlin
Falco peregrinus	Peregrine Falcon S1B, S4M, S2N Wildlife Act, SARA
Falco mexicanus	Prairie Falcon S3B, S3M, S3N
Perdix perdix	Gray Partridge
Tympanuchus phasianellus	Sharp-tailed Grouse

Buteo regalis
Ferruginous Hawk S4B, S4M, SARA
Photo: Glen & Rebecca Grambo

Scientific name	Common name
Phasianus colchicus	Ring-necked Pheasant
Rallus limicola	Virginia Rail
Porzana carolina	Sora
Fulica americana	American Coot
Grus canadensis	Sandhill Crane
Pluvialis squatarola	Black-bellied Plover
Charadrius semipalmatus	Semipalmated Plover
Charadrius melodus	Piping Plover
Charadrius vociferus	Killdeer
Himantopus mexicanus	Black-necked Stilt
Recurvirostra americana	American Avocet
Actitis macularius	Spotted Sandpiper
Tringa melanoleuca	Greater Yellowlegs
Tringa semipalmata	Willet
Tringa flavipes	Lesser Yellowlegs
Bartramia longicauda	Upland Sandpiper
Numenius americanus	Long-billed Curlew S4B, S4M Wildlife Act, SARA
Limosa haemastica	Hudsonian Godwit
Limosa fedoa	Marbled Godwit
Calidris alba	Sanderling
Calidris pusilla	Semipalmated Sandpiper
Calidris melanotos	Pectoral Sandpiper
Gallinago delicata	Wilson's Snipe
Phalaropus tricolor	Wilson's Phalarope
Phalaropus lobatus	Red-necked Phalarope
Larus pipixcan	Franklin's Gull
Larus delawarensis	Ring-billed Gull
Larus californicus	California Gull
Larus argentatus	Herring Gull
Chlidonias niger	Black Tern
Sterna hirundo	Common Tern
Sterna forsteri	Forster's Tern
Columba livia	Rock Pigeon
Zenaida macroura	Mourning Dove
Coccyzus erythropthalmus	Black-billed Cuckoo
Bubo virginianus	Great Horned Owl
Athene cunicularia	Burrowing Owl S2, Wildlife Act, SARA
Asio flammeus	Short-eared Owl S3B, S2N, SARA
Chordeiles minor	Common Nighthawk
Phalaenoptilus nuttallii	Common Poorwill S3B
Ceryle alcyon	Belted Kingfisher
Sphyrapicus varius	Yellow-bellied Sapsucker
Picoides pubescens	Downy Woodpecker

Picoides villosus	Hairy Woodpecker
Colaptes auratus	Northern Flicker
Contopus sordidulus	Western Wood-Pewee
Empidonax minimus	Least Flycatcher
Sayornis saya	Say's Phoebe
Tyrannus verticalis	Western Kingbird
Tyrannus tyrannus	Eastern Kingbird
Lanius ludovicianus	Loggerhead Shrike S4B, SARA
Vireo olivaceus	Red-eyed Vireo
Pica hudsonia	Black-billed Magpie
Corvus brachyrhyncos	American Crow
Eremophila alpestris	Horned Lark
Riparia riparia	Bank Swallow
Petrochelidon pyrrhonota	Cliff Swallow
Hirundo rustica	Barn Swallow
Poecile atricapilus (syn. Parus atricapilus)	Black-capped Chickadee
Sitta canadensis	Red-breasted Nuthatch
Troglodytes aedon	House Wren
Cistothorus platensis	Sedge Wren
Cistothorus palustris	Marsh Wren
Regulus satrapa	Golden-crowned Kinglet
Regulus calendula	Ruby-crowned Kinglet
Sialia currucoides	Mountain Bluebird
Catharus fuscescens	Veery
Catharus minimus	Gray-cheeked Thrush
Catharus ustulatus	Swainson's Thrush
Catharus guttatus	Hermit Thrush
Turdus migratorius	American Robin
Ixoreus naevius	Varied Thrush
Dumetella carolinensis	Gray Catbird
Toxostoma rufum	Brown Thrasher
Sturnus vulgaris	European Starling
Anthus spragueii	Sprague's Pipit S4B, Wildlife Act, SARA
Bombycilla cedrorum	Cedar Waxwing
Vermivora peregrina	Tennessee Warbler
Vermivora celata	Orange-crowned Warbler
Dendroica petechia	Yellow Warbler
Dendroica tigrina	Cape May Warbler
Dendroica coronata	Yellow-rumped Warbler
Dendroica striata	Blackpoll Warbler
Seiurus noveboracensis	Northern Waterthrush
Geothlypis trichas	Common Yellowthroat
Icteria virens	Yellow-breasted Chat

Lanius ludovicianus
Loggerhead Shrike S4B, SARA
Photo: Glen & Rebecca Grambo

Piranga olivacea	Scarlet Tanager S1
Pipilo maculatus	Spotted Towhee
Spizella pallida	Clay-coloured Sparrow
Spizella breweri	Brewer's Sparrow
Pooecetes gramineus	Vesper Sparrow
Chondestes grammacus	Lark Sparrow
Calamospiza melanocorys	Lark Bunting
Passerculus sandwichensis	Savannah Sparrow
Ammodramus savannarum	Grasshopper Sparrow
Ammodramus bairdii	Baird's Sparrow
Melospiza melodia	Song Sparrow
Zonotrichia albicollis	White-throated Sparrow
Zonotrichia querula	Harris' Sparrow
Zonotrichia leucophrys	White-crowned Sparrow
Junco hyemalis	Dark-eyed Junco
Calcarius mccownii	McCown's Longspur
Calcarius ornatus	Chestnut-collared Longspur
Pheucticus ludovicianus	Rose-breasted Grosbeak
Agelaius phoeniceus	Red-winged Blackbird
Sturnella neglecta	Western Meadowlark
Xanthocephalus xanthocephalus	Yellow-headed Blackbird
Euphagus cyanocephalus	Brewer's Blackbird
Quiscalus quiscula	Common Grackle
Molothrus ater	Brown-headed Cowbird
Icterus galbula	Baltimore Oriole
Carduelis tristis	American Goldfinch
Passer domesticus	House Sparrow

S listing	Status as rated by Saskatchewan Conservation Data Centre
S1	Extremely Rare
S2	Rare
S3	Rare to Uncommon
S4	Common
Wildlife Act	Listed or pending listing under the Saskatchewan Wildlife Act
SARA	Listed or pending listing under the Species at Risk A

BIBLIOGRAPHY

Space restrictions preclude a complete listing of all resources consulted in preparing this book. Those listed below are those that supplied facts used in the text or provided important background information.

All species are not created equal when assessing the impacts of species loss on ecosystems. May 22, 2003. http://www.eurekalert.org/pub_releases/2003-05/bpl-asa052203.php

Allen, Richard (ed.). 1976. Man and Nature on the Prairies.1976. Canadian Plains Studies 6. Regina, SK: Canadian Plains Research Center, University of Regina.

Ancient bison teeth provide window on past Great Plains climate, vegetation. Aug. 7, 2006. http://www.eurekalert.org/pub_releases/2006-08/uow-abt080706.php

Biggs, Lesley, and Mark Stobbe. 1991. Devine Rule in Saskatchewan: A Decade of Hope and Hardship. Saskatoon, SK: Fifth House.

Blancher, Peter. 2003. Importance of North America's Grasslands to Birds. Report to North American Commission to Environmental Cooperation.

Burlington Resources Canada Ltd. 2005. Revised Executive Summary for the environmental impact statement, 2005/2006 Freefight Lake Shallow Gas Development Project, Great Sand Hills, Saskatchewan, Project No. ES-01722-PL.09, Revised April 7 & May 5, 2005.

Costanza, R., R. d'Arge, R. de Groot, S. Farber, M. Grasso, B. Hannon, K. Limburg, S. Naeem, R.V. O'Neill, J. Paruelo, R.G. Raskin, P. Sutton, and M. van den Belt. 1997. The value of the world's ecosystem services and natural capital. Nature 387:253-360.

Cushing, Zoeth F. n.d. Reminiscences of Homesteading in Saskatchewan 1909-1961. Saskatchewan Archives Board S-A95.

Dempsey, Hugh A. 1972. Crowfoot: Chief of the Blackfeet. Norman, OK: University of Oklahoma Press.

Dempsey, Hugh A. 1978. Charcoal's World. Saskatoon, SK: Western Producer Prairie Books.

Dempsey, Hugh A. 2003. The Vengeful Wife and Other Blackfoot Stories. Norman, OK: University of Oklahoma Press.

Diaz, Polo, and Mark Nelson. 2005. "The Changing Prairie Social Landscape of Saskatchewan: The Social Capital of Rural Communities." In Managing Changing Prairie Landscapes. Todd A. Radenbaugh and Glenn C. Sutter, eds. Regina, SK: Canadian Plains Research Center, University of Regina, pp. 41-51.

Ecosystems with many plant species produce more and survive threats better. May 31, 2006. http://www.eurekalert.org/pub_releases/2006-05/nsf-ewm053106.php

Epp, Henry T. and Ian Dyck. 1983. Tracking Ancient Hunters: Prehistoric Archaeology in Saskatchewan. Regina, SK: Saskatchewan Archaeological Society.

Epp, H.T. and L. Townley-Smith. 1980. The Great Sand Hills of Saskatchewan. A report prepared for the Saskatchewan Department of the Environment on the ecology and archaeology and on resource management and land use in the Great Sand Hills of Saskatchewan.

Francis, R. Douglas. 1989. Images of the West: Changing Perceptions of the Prairies, 1690-1960. Saskatoon, SK: Western Producer Prairie Books.

Friesen, Gerald. 1987 (1993). The Canadian Prairies: A History. Toronto: University of Toronto Press.

Garden, J.F. 1999. The Palliser Triangle. Revelstoke, BC: Footprint Publishing Co.

Gelbard, J.L. and S. Harrison. 2003. Roadless habitats as refuges for native grasslands: interactions with soil, aspect and grazing. Ecological Applications 13: 404-415.

Gerry, Ann and Mike Andersen. 2003. The Ecological Impact of Human-related Disturbance in the Great Sand Hills: Exotic Plants as Indicators of Integrity. Fish and Wildlife Branch, Saskatchewan Environment,.

Goldcorp Inc. 2004. Annual Information Form : for the year ended December 31, 2003. Toronto: Goldcorp Inc.

Gray, James H. 1978. Men Against the Desert. Saskatoon, SK: Western Producer Prairie Books.

Great Sand Hills Land Use Strategy Review, Report and Recommendations Final Report June 2004.

Harel, Claude-Jean. 2006. Better habitat for Sprague's Pipit at Tugaske-area ranch. Prairie Update (Saskatchewan Watershed Authority), vol 28, Spring 2006.

Henderson, Darcy C., Elise Parker, and M. Anne Naeth. 2004. Landscape Factors and Alien Grass Invasions in the Canadian Prairies. In: Proceedings of 7th Prairie Conservation and Endangered Species Conference, February 26-28, 2004, Calgary, Alberta, pp. 202-206.

High-flying satellites give land managers the low-down on cheatgrass. June 16, 2006. http://www.eurekalert.org/pub_releases/2006-06/dnnl-hsg061506.php

Hugenholtz, C.H., and S.A. Wolfe. 2005. Recent stabilization of active sand dunes on the Canadian prairies and relation to recent climate variations. Geomorphology 68: 131-147.

Hugenholtz, C.H., and S.A. Wolfe. 2005. Biogeomorphic model of dunefield activation and stabilization on the northern Great Plains. Geomorphology 70: 53-70.

Last, William M. 1999. Geolimnology of the Great Plains of western Canada. In: Holocene Climate and Environmental Change in the Palliser Triangle: A Geoscientific Context for Evaluating the Impacts of Climate Change on the Southern Canadian Prairies. D.S. Lemmen and R.E. Vance, eds. Geological Survey of Canada, Bulletin 534, pp 23-55.

Lemmen, D.S., and R.E. Vance (eds.). 1999. Holocene Climate and Environmental Change in the Palliser Triangle: A Geoscientific Context for Evaluating the Impacts of Climate Change on the Southern Canadian Prairies. Geological Survey of Canada, Bulletin 534, 295 p.

Lemmen, D.S., and R. E. Vance. 1999. An overview of the Palliser Triangle Global Change Project. In: Holocene Climate and Environmental Change in the Palliser Triangle: A Geoscientific Context for Evaluating the Impacts of Climate Change on the Southern Canadian Prairies. D.S. Lemmen and R.E. Vance, eds. Geological Survey of Canada, Bulletin 534, pp 7-22.

Lithic Laboratories. 1989. An Archaeological Overview of Proposed Development by Lone Pine Resouces Ltd. In the Vicinity of Freefight Lake.

Long-Term Research Project Uses Ancient History Of Grasslands To Assess Effects Of Livestock Grazing In Great Plains. Nov. 14, 1997. http://www.eurekalert.org/pub_releases/1997-11/CSU-LRPU-141197.php

Lynch, Wayne. 1984. Married to the Wind. North Vancouver, BC: Whitecap Books.

Miry Creek Area History Book Committee. 2000. Bridging the centuries. Abbey, SK: Miry Creek Area History Book Committee.

Moncada, Kristine. 2003. The role of native bees in prairie restoration. Restoration and Reclamation Review, vol 8, iss 1.

Mountain Horse, Mike. 1989. My people, the Bloods. Calgary: Glenbow Museum.

Muhs, Daniel R., and Stephen A. Wolfe. 1999. Sand dunes of the northern Great Plains of Canada and the United States. In: Holocene Climate and Environmental Change in the Palliser Triangle: A Geoscientific Context for Evaluating the Impacts of Climate Change on the Southern Canadian Prairies. D.S. Lemmen and R.E. Vance, eds. Geological Survey of Canada, Bulletin 534, pp.183-197.

Noss, Reed F., and Allen Y. Cooperrider. 1994. Saving Nature's Legacy: Protecting and Restoring Biodiversity. Washington, DC: Island Press.

Order of species loss has important biodiversity consequences, grassland study reveals. Nov. 11, 2004. http://www.eurekalert.org/pub_releases/2004-11/uoc--oos110804.php

Pasitschniak-Arts, M. and F. Messier. 1998. Effects of edges and habitats on small mammals in a prairie ecosystem. Can. J. Zool. 76: 2020-2025.

Potyondi, Barry. 1995. In Palliser's Triangle. Saskatoon, SK: Purich Publishing.

Prelate History Book Committee. 1990. Our Heritage Recalled: Prelate, Saskatchewan 1908-1990. Prelate, SK: Prelate History Book Committee.

Radenbaugh, Todd. 2005. Managing changing landscapes on the northern prairies: using functional groups and guilds. In: Managing Changing Prairie Landscapes. Todd A. Radenbaugh and Glenn C. Sutter, eds. Regina, SK: Canadian Plains Research Center, University of Regina, pp. 147-159.

Radenbaugh, Todd A., and Glenn C. Sutter. 2005. The Challenges of Managing Changing Prairie Landscapes. In: Managing Changing Prairie Landscapes. Todd A. Radenbaugh and Glenn C. Sutter, eds. Regina, SK: Canadian Plains Research Center, University of Regina, pp. 1-10.

Radenbaugh, Todd A., and Glenn C. Sutter (eds.). 2005. Managing Changing Prairie Landscapes. Regina, SK: Canadian Plains Research Center, University of Regina.

Remenda, V.H., and S.J. Birks. Groundwater in the Palliser Triangle: an overview of its vulnerability and potential to archive climate information. In: Holocene Climate and Environmental Change in the Palliser Triangle: A Geoscientific Context for Evaluating the Impacts of Climate Change on the Southern Canadian Prairies. D.S. Lemmen and R.E. Vance, eds. Geological Survey of Canada, Bulletin 534, pp. 57-66.

Robertson, Heather. 1974. Salt of the Earth. Toronto: James Lorimer and Co.

Robinson, William G. (ed.) 1987. Saskatchewan Post Offices. Vancouver, BC: William Topping (privately printed.)

Saskatchewan Environment. Online 1996-current.Saskatchewan Bird Atlas. Accessed online at http://gisweb1.serm.gov.sk.ca/imf/imf.jsp?config=http://gisweb1.serm.gov.sk.ca/imf/sk/sites/Birds/BirdAtlas.xml

Savage, Candace. 2004. Prairie: A Natural History. Vancouver: Greystone Books.

Shang, Yquiang, and William M. Last. 1999. Mineralogy, lithostratigraphy, and inferred geochemical history of North Ingebrigt lake, Saskatchewan. In: Holocene Climate and Environmental Change in the Palliser Triangle: A Geoscientific Context for Evaluating the Impacts of Climate Change on the Southern Canadian Prairies. D.S. Lemmen and R.E. Vance, eds. Geological Survey of Canada, Bulletin 534, pp. 95-110.

Stunning global warming report coming: author. September 26, 2006. StarPhoenix, Saskatoon, SK.

Thompson, John Herd. 1998. Forging the Prairie West. Toronto: Oxford University Press.

Tiessen, Hugo. 1974. Old-style Prairie ranching gives way to intensive crop-and-cattle farming, Canadian Geographical Journal 88(4): 4-11.

Treaty 7 Elders and Tribal Council, Walter Hildebrandt, Dorothy First Rider, and Sarah Carter. 1996. The True Spirit and Original Intent of Treaty 7. Montreal: McGill-Queen's University Press.

Unveiling all of the consequences: Introduced plants may be causing hidden trouble. Oct. 26, 1999. http://www.eurekalert.org/pub_releases/1999-10/ESoA-Uaot-261099.php

Warnock, John W. 2004. Saskatchewan: The Roots of Discontent and Protest. Montreal: Black Rose Books.

Western Oilfield Environmental Services Ltd.. January, 1992. Executive Summary, Environmental Impact Statement, Natural Gas Development, Freefight Lake, Saskatchewan. Prepared for Lone Pine Resources Ltd.

Wolfe, S.A., D.J. Huntley, P.P. David, J. Oilerhead, D.J. Sauchyn, and G.M. MacDonald. 2001. Late 18th century drought-induced sand dune activity, Great Sand Hills, Saskatchewan. Canadian Journal of Earth Sciences 38: 105-117.

Wolfe, Stephen A. and Donald S. Lemmen. 1999. Monitoring of dune activity in the Great Sand Hills region, southwestern Saskatchewan. In: Holocene Climate and Environmental Change in the Palliser Triangle: A Geoscientific Context for Evaluating the Impacts of Climate Change on the Southern Canadian Prairies. D.S. Lemmen and R.E. Vance, eds. Geological Survey of Canada, Bulletin 534, pp. 199-210.

Wolfe, Stephen and Jeffrey Thorpe. 2005. Shifting Sands: Climate Change Impacts on Sand Hills in the Canadian Prairies and Implications for Land Use Management. In: Managing Changing Prairie Landscapes. Todd A. Radenbaugh and Glenn C. Sutter, eds. Regina, SK: Canadian Plains Research Center, University of Regina, pp 117-134.

Interviews/Personal Communications

Bowie, Eleanor. Rancher.

Fitzsimonds, Kevin. Conservation Officer, Leader Field Area.

Gummer, David. Curator of Mammalogy, Royal Alberta Museum.

Kotylak, Andrea. Habitat Stewardship Coordinator, Nature Saskatchewan.

Mathieson, J. A. Brian. Director, Petroleum Development Branch, Petroleum & Natural Gas Division, Saskatchewan Industry & Resources.

Small Legs, Edwin. Piikani Nation.

Townley-Smith, Lawrence. Agriculture and Agri-Food Canada. Co-author of 1980 GSH report.

Uhrich, Brad. Ducks Unlimited Canada.

Wrishko, Kerry. Conservation Officer, Leader Field Area.

Index

ABOUT THE AUTHORS

Rebecca L. Grambo is the award-winning author of more than 20 science and natural history books for adults and children. Her most recent releases are *Wolf: Legend, Enemy, Icon* (Firefly Books, 2005) and *Digging Canadian History* (Whitecap Books, 2006). Rebecca also writes for magazines including *Canadian Geographic, Canadian Wildlife, Nature Canada,* and is the author of a regular nature column for *Acreage Life*. A geological engineer by training, a natural history photographer, biologist and botanist by choice, she brings both the discipline of a scientist and the curiosity of a six-year-old to every project. Born and raised on the Great Plains, she now makes her home in Warman, Saskatchewan.

Dr. Branimir Gjetvaj is a Saskatoon-based biologist and photographer who specializes in western Canadian landscapes, with a focus on outdoor and nature photography. His photographs appeared in books and magazines in Canada and internationally. Branimir has been recording images of wild places for over twenty-five years. Images for the *Great Sand Hills: A Prairie Oasis* were produced over a 2 year period of intensive field work. Branimir volunteers his time and photographic skills in promoting the appreciation and protection of natural environments. Through his photography, lectures, and workshops, he tries to engage people in exploring the wonders of the natural world, and raise awareness of what we need to do to protect it.

Photo: Helen Booker